THE TAOIST ROAD TO HEALTH

THE TAOIST ROAD TO HEALTH

The Doin Method

Masao Hayashima

Translated by Harry O'North

KODANSHA INTERNATIONAL
Tokyo • New York • London

Note to the Reader: This book is presented as an aid to understanding the theories and practices of the dōin method and is not intended to replace the guidance of a qualified medical doctor. Not every suggestion applies to each particular case. Neither the author not the publisher may be found liable for any adverse effects or consequences resulting from the use of any of the suggestions in this book.

Note on orthography: All Japanese and Chinese names, both ancient and modern, appear in their original order, surname first, with the exception of the author's name on the jacket, cover, and the title and copyright pages.

Photographs illustrating poses are by Suzuki Naoto.

Distributed in the United States by Kodansha America, Inc., 114 Fifth Avenue, New York N.Y. 10011, and in the United Kingdom and continental Europe by Kodansha Europe Ltd., 95 Aldwych, London WC2B 4JF. Published by Kodansha International Ltd., 17-14 Otowa 1-chome, Bunkyo-ku, Tokyo 112-8652, and Kodansha America, Inc.
Copyright © 1997 by Masao Hayashima
All rights reserved. Printed in Japan
First edition, 1997
97 98 99 00 10 9 8 7 6 5 4 3 2 1
ISBN 4-7700-2133-X

CONTENTS

Chapter One

THE ART OF TAOIST BREATHING

Chapter Two

TAOISM IN HISTORY

Chapter THREE

BREATH, KI, AND DŌIN

Chapter FOUR

CURING CHRONIC ILLNESS

APPENDIX

THE SAKE BATH

Calligraphy by the author: large character at right means "Tao"; next line to left, "Taoist Lung Men School"; on far left, the author's name and seal.

PREFACE

I decided in high school to make medicine my career when I first experienced the deaths of people close to me and found myself wishing I could do something to cure disease. I went on to medical school and vividly recall the sobering moment when a professor observed that a doctor can cure only a fraction of the people he treats. In many of the most serious cases, the body either cures itself or the patient dies. I went through my internship and residency, then in 1982 started my own practice. In those first years on my own, I would stay up all night with patients suffering from acute infections and take great satisfaction in curing them with Western medical techniques. But the longer I practiced, the more I found how many cases could not be cured, and how the number of chronic sufferers kept increasing. Acute attacks, such as acute bronchitis or bladder infections, may be completely cured with the appropriate antibiotic. But if the doctor does not choose the right one, or if the patient does not respond to treatment, the disease can become intractable. In the case of chronic bronchitis, for example, the patient can spend the rest of his or her life alternating between small gains and setbacks. With chronic diseases such as diabetes, rheumatism, atopic dermatitis, and inflammations of the liver or kidneys, it is all the doctor can do to hold the diseases in check. Doctors cannot even cure the common cold. All we can do is prescribe drugs for fever, coughing, or nasal congestion. We simply prescribe for the symptoms—a druggist or a computer could do the same. When someone with rheumatism comes to a clinic, the doctor can do nothing more than prescribe an analgesic for the pain and hope that the disease is not malignant rheumatoid arthritis that can affect other internal organs. The disease will stay with the patient forever, and all the doctor can really do is sympathize.

Over the years, patients kept coming to my clinic, and I kept examining them but was unable to cure them all through Western medical techniques. I gradually became disillusioned with the entire Western approach to disease. We can learn all we want about the biological composition of the cell, but that is not real medicine.

Then my mother developed a hyperthyroid condition and came to my clinic for treatment. But the drugs I prescribed caused an allergic reaction, and we were forced to abandon them. We were also unwilling to risk the side effects of radiation therapy. But then my younger brother told her about the dōin method, and she tried it. She found that it alleviated her symptoms and that she was able to hold the disorder in check without drugs of any kind.

My health too began to suffer from the demands of a full-time practice coupled with housework and raising children. My brother encouraged me to try dōin as well. I did so and began attending lectures, where I learned from Dr. Hayashima Masao about the five-thousand-year history of *dōin* (*tao-yin* in the original Chinese) in China and the Taoist philosophy of Lao Tzu. I soon realized that I had finally found the medical approach I had been looking for all those years. I realized that I had never felt truly at home with the Western approach to disease, because it is based solely on the intellect, not on the heart. Dōin is the antithesis of this—it is a simple approach that anyone can apply. The great truths of nature are simple and straightforward; they do not require complex theories to understand.

I used to wake up in the morning groggy and exhausted, feeling like Gulliver tied to the ground by countless ropes. I thought I was just overtired and experiencing a touch of low blood pressure, never realizing that the true cause was a stomach problem. I was the picture of ill health.

But as I practiced dōin each day, I felt my body recover; it became more supple and easier in its movements. Today I feel constantly invigorated. I personally experienced the curative effects of the dōin method and learned that health depends on absorbing *ki* (*ch'i* in the original Chinese) from the natural world and causing it to circulate throughout the body, while at the same time purging stagnant and harmful ki. I learned that the body is intimately connected to the seasons, to periods of hot and cold, wet and dry, and also to the emotions, joy and anger, pleasure and pain.

It is not enough simply to scientifically treat the human body as a biological organism. Western medicine has yet to recognize the unknown potential in each of us. We allow this state of ignorance to continue at our peril. The Eastern approach of dōin is diametrically opposed; it invites us to reexamine our basic assumptions about health care and restructure our priorities in our daily lives. This is true healing. The more people who learn the dōin method, the better for the future of us all.

Dr. Makita Junko

The author in meditation.

INTRODUCTORY REMARKS

Hayashima Daisensei, his wife Myōzui Sensei, and his daughter Myōchō Sensei came into my life about five years ago. I say "came into" because they approached me for some international business advice when I was running my own consulting company in Tokyo. Since that time many things have changed. I have changed professions, and now, instead of being an adviser to the Hayashimas, I am one of their students learning dōin. I stress the fact that I am a student and a novice and freely admit that it took me a long time to wake up to the benefits of Daisensei's teachings. Even now, though I have already benefited tremendously from dōin, I know that I have taken only the first steps toward a much happier and healthier life.

A Tale of Two Festivals

The first time I sought Daisensei's advise I was embroiled in a messy situation in my consulting business—a confrontation filled with deceit, treachery, and intrigue. Never before had I felt so little confidence in my ability to make a decision. I had no idea what to do, and many decisions had to be made to protect me, my business partners, and my clients. I explained the convoluted situation to Daisensei as best I could, admitted I was at a loss, and waited for his response.

That day he told me three things that were both simple and profound. One of these I would like to share with you. Daisensei said that there were two festivals held at the same time in two adjoining prefectures. One was held to celebrate "victory," the other "preparing for war." People in the two prefectures were welcome to attend either festival. Every year, about one half of the people chose the festival with the war preparation theme and the other half chose the festival with the victory theme. If I were to choose, Daisensei then asked me, which festival would I attend?

Along with many things he said that day, I have to admit that I did not really understand how this story would help me with my immediate problems. It seemed clear to me that any sane person would go to the festival that celebrates victory. Who would want to go to an event that focuses on getting ready for war? I declared that I wanted to go to the victory festival, and Daisensei nodded his head. That was that, and we never spoke of it again until three years later.

It took me three years and lots of pain in my body to realize that I was regularly choosing the war festival. I lived in constant preparation for battle, engaging in an occasional skirmish to keep me alert and sharp. In actual fact, I was fooling myself in thinking I was choosing victory. My body, when I finally learned to acknowledge it, told me something quite different.

This is one of the lessons that dōin has to teach—there is no fooling the body. Once you establish a clear communication channel (through the unimpeded flow of ki), your body lets you know when you are making decisions that are right for you and objects strongly when you have chosen a destructive path.

Listening to Your Body, Listening with Your Body

As I write this, I stop from time to time to check in with my body. Although I have vastly improved, I still have telltale signs of battle preparation. I feel it in my left shoulder, upper back, and neck. Predictably it is worse when I am in prolonged stressful situations. Since I currently work in Japan as an executive search consultant (less charitably referred to as a "headhunter"), my role as hunter offers many opportunities for battle.

But I have no intention of spending the rest of my life going to the festival which celebrates preparing for war. I freely admit I yearn for the victory festival. My body tells me this. When my body is clear, supple, free of pain and disease, I know that I am celebrating victory.

When I first started on this adventure, sometime after Daisensei told me the tale of the two festivals, I was totally out of touch with my body and had completely suppressed daily pain and discomfort. Daisensei and his daughter Myōchō Sensei would often ask me—how is your body today? Is it comfortable? I did not really understand the question. My body was fine, I felt nothing, and I couldn't help but wonder what they were talking about. Once in a while I would have a headache, sinus problems, and digestive disturbances, for which I would take some over-the-counter medicine. If I was really sick I would go to a doctor, rest up, and take prescription medicine. So what did they mean by a comfortable body?

A series of things happened over a year or so that opened my eyes to what they meant. I began to realize that I was holding a tremendous amount of pain in my body. I had massages that reduced me to tears, the inner corners of my eyes were often red, I had a kind of tingling in my right foot, I could digest fewer and fewer foods. The last straw was a nagging pain and stiffness in my hands that grew so intense that I couldn't use the computer. My body was most definitely not comfortable and was demanding that I take notice.

Panicking, I went to various doctors and heard about cancer, neurological disorders, and a host of other terrifying maladies. After a battery of tests I learned there was nothing seriously wrong with me yet. I was exhausted and my body needed rest and healing. Clearly I had been living a life destructive to my entire being.

I have few conventional bad habits. I do not smoke, drink, or eat to excess. And I exercise regularly. My most serious shortcoming is probably overwork, or more precisely an excessive focus on work. But what was I to do—quit my job, leave Tokyo and the world of headhunting for a kinder and gentler place? Believe me, I thought about it seriously, and I had an escape plan ready. But somehow I couldn't go through with it. I knew there was an important lesson to be learned, and running away would only delay the learning. Instead, I chose complete surrender to the needs of my body (this was not so difficult as I was so tired I had little energy to do anything). I was determined to learn to listen with humility and respect.

The fog was beginning to lift, and I could see that this was what the dōin method was all about. After several years of knowing about the dōin body movements—through reading and seminars—I began to see the simple movements as constituting a friendly dialogue with the body. I became a daily practitioner of seven movements and am adding others as time passes. I can honestly say that I am now in touch with my body and, when I choose to listen, it lets me know whether or not it is comfortable. When its not comfortable, I know there is something wrong: most often when I am getting ready for some useless and self-destructive battle.

Not only have I learned to listen to my body, I am also getting a sense of what it means to listen *with* the body. When the body's ki is flowing positively and freely, good decisions come naturally. In other words, you can sense the best course of action with your body—a sort of listening with the body.

We all have had times when our timing was perfect, when we instinctively knew what to do, took action and had success. It may have been in sport, business, a personal or family situation. I have proven to myself over the last year that this is not only a matter of luck or mental preparedness. The most important thing is to have positive ki, and then these times and successes happen much more frequently. Fortunately, positive ki can be cultivated and developed. Some people seem to know how to do it instinctively. For others like me who have suppressed the instinct, dōin teaches many simple ways to develop ki. All it takes is commitment and a small amount of time. I spend about ten minutes twice a day doing dōin exercises and have benefited immensely. When my body tells me to spend more time (and when I choose to listen), I take time out in the middle of the day to do one or two exercises. This always gives me a lift and shifts the flow of ki in a more positive direction.

I admit that I don't always listen to what my body says, and without fail this is a mistake. I know when my ki is blocked or negative in some way, and if I continue to press forward regardless, it always results in some kind of failure. For me this might mean a disagreement with a colleague, making a bad decision about a business matter, suffering from eating or drinking something that is not right for me at the time, or even something so trivial as tripping while going down the stairs. At these times I would be much better off if I stopped, took a break, breathed deeply, and followed the advice of my body.

Although I took up dōin to relieve stress and pain, I have had an additional benefit. One of the dōin movements I do is called *anpuku* and assists digestion and elimination (see p. 94). I have been doing this exercise daily for ten months and have gradually noticed a reduction in the layer of fat around my midsection. I have not made any conscious change in diet and am exercising somewhat less than I have in the past. I had resigned myself to living with this bit of jello since it has been with me since childhood and has responded to neither diet nor exercise. Well, it is almost gone now—quite extraordinary, and so easy.

The Joy of the Sake Bath

One of the most enjoyable dōin practices to promote health, youth-fulness, and positive ki is the sake bath. For the last six months I have had at least one sake bath a day, with no intention of stopping—whether I am traveling or not. I started the practice as part of "listening to my body" and continue because it is so effective at promoting positive ki and ridding the body of bad ki, not to speak of the exquisite sensual experience it offers.

I was the kind of person who rarely took a real bath. Who had the time? A shower was much quicker and easier. By now you will have realized that this refers back to the two festivals—preparing for war leaves you with precious little time for a bath. If you decide to treat yourself to a daily sake bath you can take this as a sign that you are well on your way to celebrating victory.

Because my body enjoys the bath so much, I hate to intellectualize the benefits. However, since starting this practice I have come across several articles from diverse sources that explain the scientific benefit of warming the body in this way. As Daisensei will explain in this book, the sake adds to the beneficial effects of the bath by helping the warmth penetrate the body and stimulate circulation. I am usually pink all over by the time I get out.

My favorite is the *biba-zake* bath, and I always take some *biba-zake* in powdered form when I travel. It may seem like a wild extravagance, but I would suggest that it is one well worth indulging in. With the improved ki that follows, you will surely generate all the income you need to pay for the sake.

As Daisensei said to me some time ago: "Have a sake bath every day. It will change your life." He was right. It did and still does—in many, many ways.

Deborah Wetmore

THE ART OF
TAOIST BREATHING

A Man Who Walks on All Fours

I know a man whose personal health regimen involves walking on all fours when he is in his own room at home. He is over eighty, but his legs and back are as strong as a much younger man's. Years and years before, someone had told him, "The human body has not yet adapted to walking upright. When we do, the stress opens the door to various illnesses." Ever since, he has walked on all fours when at home.

The Taoist term *tao-yin* (*dōin* in Japanese, which I shall use henceforth since it is the term with which I am most intimately familiar) is hard to define. To some, dōin practices look rather like other physical exercises, and the more complex forms may resemble yoga. One effective way of characterizing the dōin art is to suggest that it involves imitating birds and other animals. The reason that I began this chapter with the elderly man who walks on all fours is that it is a perfect example of such copying. Here is someone who doesn't know the first thing about dōin practices and yet has successfully exploited them in their most elemental form for health preservation and rejuvenation. It was probably through just such experimentation that the art was first developed in China over five thousand years ago.

A Secret Recipe for Rejuvenation from Ancient China

For five millennia, the art of dōin has been China's greatest health secret. After much research and testing, I have developed what I feel is the most successful way to apply its teachings to people today. At its most basic level, dōin is a means to recover youthful vitality. Applying it, you can cure a variety of imbalances and diseases.

After reaching the age of twenty or so, we begin to age. The skin

The author at the Nihon Dōkan headquarters.

loses its luster and elasticity. We find its harder to climb the stairs. The legs and back start to hurt, and we lose our "get up and go." With the exception of outright illness, we all accept this as the inevitable effects of growing older, and Western medicine can as yet do almost nothing to counteract it. It is taken as a given that there is no fountain of youth. But with the practice of dōin it is possible to retain youthful vigor almost indefinitely. Moreover, you can literally turn back the clock and make an old body young again.

When I was in China before the Second World War, I had the opportunity to observe Taoist adepts in action as they practiced dōin. They did not teach me directly, of course; I was allowed to watch, but the rest was up to me. What particularly amazed me was the youthful appearance of the women at the training center. All of them were devoting themselves to mastering the dōin method, and all appeared to be around twenty years old. I discovered later, though, that not one of them was under fifty. Dōin preserves the natural youth of the body, and prevents it from aging. This of course applies to men as well; a man you think could not be more than thirty may turn out to be seventy. A number of years ago, the popular Japanese singer Sada Masashi related in an interview for a weekly magazine how during a trip to China he had visited a Taoist training temple. He remarked in particular about the people pursuing dōin there, all of whom were easily over one hundred years old!

In ancient China, those who strove to live at one with nature were referred to as Taoists, or "adepts of the Way," a mode of living that had its roots in the philosophy of Lao Tzu. Those adepts may be contrasted with the followers of Confucius, a prescriptive philosopher devoted to determining how a person should control his or her life. By contrast, Taoists—following the thought of Lao Tzu—believed that the highest mode of living was that in which both mind and body were allowed to act according to natural inclination. For them, sickness and aging were thought to arise when some element of daily life stood in opposition to nature, and if that element could be corrected, then illness would cure itself and further illness would be avoided. In this way, it was thought, one could live to a great age, both youthful and happy.

Actually, this philosophy was not created by Lao Tzu alone. It was instead the outgrowth of ancient Chinese thought that developed long before Lao Tzu's writings appeared. Those beliefs were later systematized and ascribed to a single source which we now know as Lao Tzu, who was not an actual individual but instead the symbol of an entire intellectual system.

Based on the ideals of Lao Tzu, Taoists constantly searched for methods to preserve the body's essential nature. One technique early Taoists used was to examine the habits of animals in the wild. They made three basic discoveries:

1. The bodies of animals never move in just one direction; there is always a counter-movement as well.

2. Animals employ a special method of breathing (for example, before turtles enter the water, they always breathe as deeply as possible by bending their heads far back).

3. Animals do not fall prey to many of our diseases. In their natural environment, animals do not catch colds, for example, or have diarrhea. Nor do they age the way we do; when they reach the end of their lives, the well of life simply runs dry, as it were.

Were we to move and breathe as the animals do, thought the Taoists, then we too could avoid illness and live out our lives in health. It was to that purpose that for thousands of years they experimented on themselves and developed various techniques, passing on by word of mouth their secret recipes for longevity. The dōin method is the result of those millennia of experimentation. The strength of dōin is that it is not the product of one or two people but is instead the culmination of five thousand years of experimentation by tens of thousands.

When Taoists pursued the question of what was at the very basis of life lived in accord with natural rhythms, they hit upon the central concept of *ch'i* or *ki*. The discovery of ki brought about great development in the dōin art. It will be discussed in detail hereafter.

Breathing and Movement to Cleanse the Body

According to the science of ki, the cause of illness and aging is the accumulation of harmful ki. To rid the body of this harmful ki, you must breathe while stimulating the *tsubo*—points along the internal meridians that channel ki through the body. Deep breathing purges waste and carbon dioxide from the system and simultaneously replenishes the blood with fresh ki (which might be equated with oxygen). Taken out of the body, blood is simply blood and nothing more, but when circulating inside the body it binds with ki and is called "ki-rich blood." When a physical imbalance occurs through cold or fatigue, the blood in the internal organs and joints stagnates. In places where the old, bad blood has stagnated, fresh blood cannot circulate, and illness or symptoms of aging develop. Back pain is one such example.

Fresh blood is red and pure. Bad blood flows black, heavy, and viscid. When bad blood reaches the extremities, it stagnates in the capillaries, increasing its deleterious effects. There is no other way to rid the body of this old blood than by cleansing it with a fresh supply. But this is difficult when the old, viscid blood has obstructed the capillary network. If this bad blood cannot be eliminated, the condition of the blood goes from bad to worse, beginning a vicious cycle.

One of the purposes of the dōin method is to stimulate the circulation of ki-rich blood by slow breathing and efficient muscle movement. By stimulating all parts of the body with such exercises, the stagnant bad blood and ki is encouraged to flow out through the lungs and skin or is purified in the kidneys and is eliminated as waste. This, then, is how the dōin method cures disease and prevents aging. Fresh ki in the cells rejuvenates. Medical texts say that it requires seven years for the body to renew all its cells, but with dōin, they are reinvigorated immediately. Patients over fifty with rheumatism or goiter who come to my office can take ten years off their ages literally in one week. Not only cells but blood, skin, muscles, and bones also must renew themselves. Through the dōin method, stagnant harmful ki is driven out and the blood is purified. That in turn purifies the bones, cells, and skin, with the result that fatigue is instantly relieved and prevented from reoccurring.

How I Became the Head of the Lung Men School of Taoism

Let me share an episode that demonstrates something of the efficacy of the dōin method. It happened when I visited Taiwan in 1969. A man named Ch'en Yung-sheng called on me at my hotel. He was an official at the great Taoist establishment Szu Han T'ien Shih Fu (Office of the Celestial Master who Aided the Han Dynasty), and many Japanese students of Taoism had received instruction from him. He had learned of me through the Japanese Taoist scholar Kubo Noritada of Tokyo University. He told me that the wife of the head of a certain Taiwanese bank was ill. She couldn't walk, was suffering from incontinence, and was also feared to be growing mentally unstable. They asked me if I could help her through dōin.

I knew immediately that I could improve her physical problems, but I could not assess her mental condition without seeing her first. In Japan, I had had success with neurosis and manic-depression, but if she were indeed suffering from mental problems, I knew it would be difficult to help her with my limited Chinese. But the way that she bowed when we were introduced suggested to me that her mental condition was not in fact the problem, and I thereupon agreed to work with her. After three days of instruction in dōin, she was walking and could go to the bathroom by herself.

Others soon heard of the speed and efficacy of my dōin treatments, and one day I was visited by a friend of Mr. Ch'en's named Chiang Chia-chin. He was the head of the Lung Men (Dragon Gate) school of Taoism, one of the institutions where dōin is practiced. He had met the banker and seen the effects of my treatment of the banker's wife, and so he had asked to be introduced to me. Mr. Chiang told me that although he was the twelfth head of the Lung Men school, he was not as versed in dōin practices per se as I was. He volunteered to teach me all he knew of the art and then make me his successor as thirteenth head of the school. Although dōin was developed in China, there are few Taoists actually practicing the art in China today, and the dōin techniques have become considerably limited. Mr. Chiang therefore hoped that I would agree to take over the school and pass on the art more widely. I accepted his offer and formally become the school's thirteenth head. I was the first foreigner to attain that position, an

The author around time of becoming thirteenth master of the Lung Men school and advisor to the Szu Han T'ien Shih Fu, Taiwan.

honor that I received because the dōin techniques I resuscitated were recognized by the Chinese Taoist establishment as legitimate and orthodox.

In my late twenties I had gone to China as a soldier during the war. When I could find the time, I visited Confucian shrines and Taoist temples, and as I mentioned earlier, I learned what I could of dōin from the adepts as they practiced, played with the children, and taught them Chinese characters.

I was wounded at Kueilin and returned to Japan to work in the shipyards of Tokyo. At that time I studied aiki-jutsu (the predecessor of aikidō) and karate. As soon as I had established something of a reputation in martial arts, I was made a special bodyguard to the army high command, and along with thirty other specialists was posted to Southeast Asia. For two years thereafter I threw myself into the hazardous life of a bodyguard, practicing martial arts and participating in contests with the other bodyguards. In Thailand I also learned the very violent techniques of Thai kick-boxing.

Thanks to my study of aiki-jutsu, dōin, and Taoism, I began teaching at the police academy after the war, specializing in aiki-jutsu—

based techniques to be used during arrests. Aiki-jutsu involves breathing techniques and energizes the practitioner through improved flow of ki, and so even when a policeman was suffering from a headache or back pain, he found himself cured while in class practicing arrest techniques.

When I reached fifty, I began teaching my own brand of dōin to the general public. I opened a school in the city of Kamakura that included a training room, where I instructed a large number of students, and another area for examination and treatment. I also gave public lectures, appeared on television, and started a publishing career.

After obtaining the requisite passport as a martial arts instructor, I spent a half a year traveling in Europe. Later I was invited to participate in the movement to popularize brown rice organized by George Osawa, and in that capacity I visited France, Germany, Switzerland, the Netherlands, and Belgium, where my dōin methods were featured in the newspapers. Witnesses were amazed by, for example, the way dōin relieved otherwise inoperable varicose veins in a manner of hours. It was even called a magic remedy, receiving considerable acclaim. Then in 1980 I opened the Nihon Dōkan for the teaching of Taoism, and I have been teaching dōin there ever since.

The Difference between the Dōin Method and Other Health Regimes

There are an extraordinary number of different approaches to health worldwide, and it is extremely hard for a person to choose one, as all are reputed to be effective. I would like at this point to compare dōin to several of these other health programs.

The first of these is yoga, perhaps the best-known approach to health through physical movement and one that is gaining popularity of late, especially among women. Yoga was not originally a health practice at all, but instead an austerity regimen wherein the adept tested his physical limits. Unlike dōin, it does not possess the means to combat a wide variety of diseases. Yoga positions, moreover, require special practice and are not possible for everyone.

By contrast, dōin is devoted to returning the body to its natural foundations, and it therefore does not require any unnatural and painful movements. Dōin may call for bending the legs, for example, but it does not insist that those incapable of doing so persist until they have done it. It is efficacious even when the practitioner bends the legs only as far as is comfortable. And if they are completely unbendable, a different exercise is substituted. One of dōin's more important characteristics is that it can be applied regardless of gender or age. Even children can profit from it.

Health approaches based on diet are also popular, particularly vegetarianism or limiting intake to a single type of food. It is true, of course, that a vegetarian diet does cleanse the blood, and it is also a fact that it can remove skin discolorations. I met an elderly man who had long subscribed to a vegetarian diet, and I was amazed at how healthy his skin looked. But after we had finished talking and he stood up to go, I immediately saw that there was nothing young about his bent posture and tottering walk. Did a vegetarian diet really contribute much to his health? A vegetarian diet may be good for external appearance, but it cannot prevent aging of the legs and internal organs. A system that only concentrates on exteriors and does not rejuvenate internally is not a true route to health. Dōin is. It does not make food a major issue; any diet is acceptable as long as it is balanced and taken in moderation. Dōin will maintain health no matter what the diet.

There are also many approaches that bear the name of their originators. Many may indeed have advantages, but they are all limited by the fact that they were each developed by a single person and are thus by definition limited in perspective. These approaches may work as long as the inventor and the user share the same physical characteristics, but they fail when applied to those who don't fit that profile. Dōin, on the other hand, was developed over five thousand years by a vast number of people, and it is therefore universal in application.

Sports, too, especially jogging, have recently become popular methods to maintain health. But I find it problematic to equate temporary improvements in strength and endurance with improvements in overall health. As I mentioned before, the road to health is through improving the circulation of ki-rich blood and eliminating harmful ki. Through sports, the body generates abnormal amounts of chemicals that cause fatigue. As sports provide no particular way to eliminate waste, harmful ki gradually accumulates and the body is thrown into imbalance. Athletes have surprisingly short life spans on the average. Even among Olympians, the hard training for the games tells on their bodies afterward. There is a limit to everything, and, as the proverb says, "too much is as bad as too little."

Eliminating Germs rather than Destroying Them

The way that the dōin method cures disease is by returning the body to its natural condition. This is a particular characteristic of the art. It places primary value on the natural condition of the body and cures without ever opposing that nature. This approach is shared by other Eastern curative methods. Western medicine—now generally synonymous with modern medicine—opposes nature and cures by altering it.

Consider pulmonary tuberculosis. Whereas modern medicine attempts to cure the disease by suppressing the action of the bacillus, dōin simply eliminates the bacilli from the system. It does this through a special breathing technique that stimulates the circulation of ki-rich blood. The blood vessels in the lungs are thus stimulated, restoring functionality to the lungs themselves. The bacilli have no more opportunity to reproduce, and they are eliminated as waste.

People do not normally fill their lungs entirely with air, and for this reason the ki in the lungs is not fully replenished. Bacteria can then invade and reproduce, causing dysfunction and disease. But if the ki in the lungs is regularly replenished, the bacilli cannot reproduce even if they invade, and they are instead eliminated.

Tsubo: The Body's Vital Points

Many readers will have already heard of meridians, the lines throughout the body upon which the points or nodes called *tsubo* are located. To take an example, the "kidney meridian" is the line that connects the tsubo related to that organ. These tsubo are what are called "vital points" in martial arts, the striking of which can cause damage to seemingly unrelated organs. There is a spot in the arch of the foot that when hit can result in injury to the kidney, and in the worst instances cause death. But unlike a nerve, the meridian that connects the tsubo of the arch of the foot with the kidney is invisible. It cannot be discovered by dissection. Dōin works by stimulating these meridians, which in turn revivifies the flow of ki-rich blood. Although the concept of ki-rich blood is not as well known as that of meridian stimulation, masters of *shiatsu* (literally "finger pressure") have corroborated its existence in their clinical experience of applying finger pressure on meridians and tsubo. At the mention of curing disease by stimulating the meridians, most people immediately think of shiatsu, acupuncture, and moxibustion. But these approaches are somewhat different from dōin. Shiatsu practitioners press on tsubo with their thumbs, acupuncture pierces them with needles, and moxibustion stimulates them with heat. Their methods differ, but all directly stimulate the tsubo along the meridians. Dōin, by contrast, stimulates the meridians indirectly, through muscle movement and specialized breathing techniques. As explained earlier, through the concerted use of movement and breathing, dōin improves the flow of ki-enriched blood, which instantly eliminates the harmful ki from the body. Its effect, therefore, is very different from that obtained by shiatsu, acupuncture, and moxibustion. First, shiatsu does not involve breath training. Fresh ki is therefore not sufficiently introduced into the system, nor is harmful ki as completely eliminated as it is in dōin. Second, it is remarkably difficult to accurately stimulate tsubo from the outside. But since dōin works through physical movement and is designed to directly stimulate the meridians, anyone can do it simply and effectively.

Seen in this light, it is easy to understand why dōin has a much higher rate of effectiveness than shiatsu. For example, when one undergoes shiatsu massage for a sore shoulder, the symptoms may be temporarily eased, but the following day the shoulder is sore again. This is because the bad blood has only been temporarily massaged out. But as long as the ki-rich blood is not stimulated, the bad blood will accumulate again over time. In dōin, by contrast, the harmful ki is expelled from the body and the ki-rich blood is revivified, resulting in a fundamental cure.

Once you learn dōin, you can apply it anytime and anywhere. You do not need to go to a specialist, as you must in the case of shiatsu, acupuncture, or moxibustion.

The Benefits of the Dōin Method

Let me now enumerate the characteristics of the dōin approach to health, disease treatment, and rejuvenation:

1. Not only is dōin effective against disorders and chronic problems that do not respond to modern medicine, it can rejuvenate the body and raise it to an even higher state of health.

2. It goes to work immediately. In the quickest cases it can show results the very day it is begun. Even chronic diseases can be cured in a short time.

3. Since, as a general rule, it does not use drugs or have any dietary restrictions, there are absolutely no harmful side effects.

4. No special preparation or training is required; anyone can begin any time and employ its methods daily even at home.

5. Not only is it good for general improvement of health, but there are special techniques for various types of symptoms, making it applicable to a wide variety of illnesses.

The complaints that commonly plague modern people—back pain, hemorrhoids, obesity, constipation—form an endless list. Although generally not immediately life threatening, they can't be dealt with effectively by modern science. Most people give up trying to find a cure and simply endure their discomfort. Is this conducive to a happy life?

Massage of the fingers and toes is a secret of long life

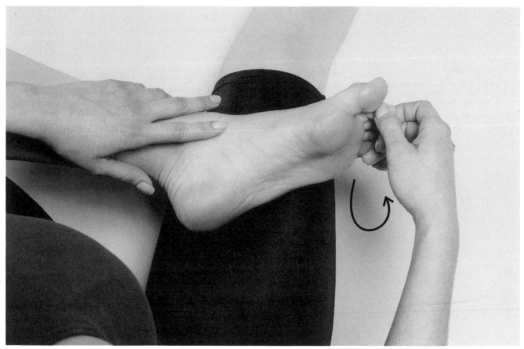

Aging begins in the feet. Try to find the time to practice this technique.

If you apply the techniques of dōin, however, you can easily recover your health by treating the fundamental causes of pain. This is healing in the truest sense of the word.

In Chapter Four, I will introduce concrete techniques for dealing with various health problems. For the present, I will simply explain one way to maintain youth and health. Every day for thirty minutes, gently massage your fingers and toes one by one. It sounds incredibly easy, but this encourages the ki you take into your lungs to flow to the very ends of your hands and feet, stimulating the flow of ki-rich blood and restoring health to the body.

At first, the fingers and toes are stiff and are hard to manipulate. But as soon as the flow of ki-rich blood is stimulated, they immediately become flexible. Soon the sense of stress is relieved, discomfort disappears, and anxiousness fades away. If you continue the practice, the shape of the fingers and toes and the condition of the nails will improve. But more important than anything else, this practice is a secret for longevity.

1. Take the end of one of your thumbs by your other thumb and forefinger and gently twist it.

2. As you twist it, move in a massaging motion down to where the thumb joins to the hand.

3. Next do the same to the forefinger and the other fingers.

4. After finishing all five digits, massage those on the other hand the same way.

TWO

TAOISM IN HISTORY

The Philosophy of the Yellow Emperor and Lao Tzu

In the compendium of thought entitled *Lao Tzu*, attributed to a philosopher of the same name, the following passage appears:

> *Fame or flesh: which is more immediate?*
> *Health or wealth: which is more important?*
> *Gain or loss: which is more burdensome?*
> *Deep attachment brings great expense;*
> *Vast hoarding brings certain loss.*
> *To know sufficiency is to avoid shame;*
> *To know limitations is to avoid danger.*
> *This is the way to obtain eternal life.*

With these words, Lao Tzu tells us that our most important possession is our own body. If we know what is sufficient to our needs and if we control our desires, we will lead a longer and more fulfilling life.

The Taoist approach to life goes back to the Yellow Emperor (Huang Ti), a legendary sage reputed to have unified China for the first time in the twenty-sixth century B.C.E. He took the hues and shapes of clouds and the way that they rose into the sky as indicators for how to order the state. He was, in fact, basing his political rule on the principle of ki. This way of thinking was later adopted by sages and emperors. Then in the third century B.C.E., Lao Tzu expounded the philosophy that taking in the ki of heaven and earth was the highest form of human existence.

The oldest medical classic in China, the *Inner Classic of the Yellow Emperor (Huang Ti Nei Ching)*, which was transmitted early to Japan and which even today is respected as a classical source for acupuncture and

Painting of Lao Tzu displayed in Nihon Dōkan.

moxibustion, states that in the age of the Yellow Emperor, dōin was already being used for treating illness. The Taoist way of life, based on the thought of the Yellow Emperor and Lao Tzu, was from early times explored as a route to cultivate the fundamentals of health and longevity. It was this Taoist philosophy, for example, that caused the first emperor of the Ch'in, Ch'in Shih Huang Ti, to send hermit sages into the eastern ocean on a quest for immortality. The essence of the thought of the Taoist Immortals was the search for that in the human body which did not deteriorate. This Taoist principle was later adopted into Confucianism, Moism (the thought of Mo Tzu or Micius), Buddhism, and other philosophies. It also led to the formation of Chinese medicine and the dōin method. The dōin method, with its emphasis on breathing, formed the basis for kung fu, t'ai chi ch'uän, and other disciplines.

The *Wu Ch'in Hsi* of the Physician Hua T'o

At the end of the Later Han Dynasty (the end of the second century C.E.), there lived a great man of medicine named Hua T'o. He is important in the annals of medical science for being the first to use anesthesia. His treatise *Wu Ch'in Hsi* links breathing to natural movement. *Wu ch'in* means "five animals" (specifically, monkeys, bears, tigers, deer, and birds), and as the title implies, the work sets up a system of exercises based on the detailed observation of animals in the wild, focusing on how, for example, they breathe when they bend their bodies, or on whether they inhale or exhale when they stretch. Hua T'o and his disciples personally applied these rules of breathing-based movement, and their youthful appearance and energy never left them.

Their system developed a huge following and exerted an influence

Wu Ch'in Hsi: Imitating various animals

Monkey

Tiger

Bear

Deer

Bird

on many health practices. This was the beginning of the codification of dōin. Hua T'o was at length summoned to cure the head pains of the autocrat Ts'ao Ts'ao, founder of the Wei dynasty, but when he attempted to insert acupuncture needles, Ts'ao Ts'ao became enraged and had him executed. It is said that Hua T'o was more than one hundred years old at the time.

Dōin Described in a Book from Mawangtui

Some readers may recall the discovery of a mummy found in one of the Mawangtui tombs in the Chinese city of Ch'ang-sha. The female mummy was two thousand years old but looked almost as though she were just sleeping. During the excavation a diagram on silk was also discovered that shows dōin being practiced. The more than forty poses therein were tentatively restored by Professor Serizawa Katsusuke, then a professor at Tokyo University of Education. He has observed, "In this two-thousand-year-old system of exercises are found principles now considered to be at the forefront of modern medicine. It views human beings not as automata or robots but as organic wholes. It is truly marvelous, a way of thought that grew out of the techniques of close empirical observation characteristic of Eastern medicine." Professor Serizawa is himself a prime authority on Eastern health practices. It is indeed remarkable that the techniques of dōin should have been employed by the Chinese aristocracy two millennia ago.

The restoration of the diagram was later completed in China on the basis of further research. I would now like to explain the effects of the techniques of dōin practiced in that era through the analysis of this remarkable cultural artifact. I have given a tentative number to

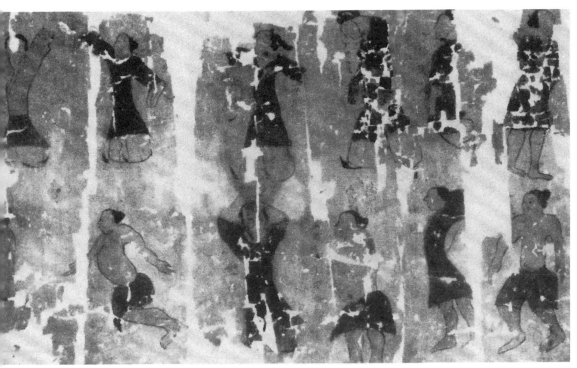

Ancient drawing on silk showing dōin poses.

each of the poses and have had them redrawn. It will become clear that dōin from more than two thousand years ago can have more health benefits than modern approaches to exercise.

1. Caption: "Conducting yin and yang by a staff." A woman bends at the waist, with one hip higher than the other. She supports herself by holding a long staff in both hands, resting one end on the ground. (Excellent for increasing sexual vitality.)

2. Caption: "Hawk Back." A person (a woman?) stands straight up, holding the arms out horizontally. (For heart disease, bronchial asthma, chronic bronchitis.)

3. No caption. A woman stands facing to her right, arms at her sides. (Sexual revitalization, stops aging and promotes rejuvenation.)

4. No caption. A woman stands with her right arm to her side, palm facing backward and slightly up. The left arm is in the same attitude as the right, in the basic position for the exercise called swaiso (see Chapter Three). (Cures stiffening of the arms and shoulders that comes with age.)

5. Caption illegible. A woman stands facing to her right with her right arm raised high. Her left arm hangs by her side. Torsion is the term for head movement being different from body movement—a basic cure-all technique in dōin. (For fatigue.)

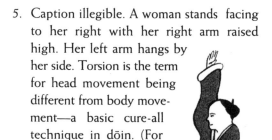

6. No caption. A woman bends forward at the waist with her hands hanging down, as if holding something. (Strengthens the waist and the back, good for general debility.)

7. Caption illegible. A man stands with his upper body twisted to the right and both arms held level in front of him. (For lower back pain, and tightness from the shoulder blades down the back.)

9. No caption. A person, apparently a woman, stands facing the right with both arms to her sides. (Same as no. 7.)

8. No caption. A woman stands slightly bent at the hips with both arms slanting downward. (For very tight shoulder muscles, stroke, and paralysis.)

10. Caption: "Drawing out deafness." A woman stands with hunched shoulders, arms out to the sides, and legs apart.

11. Caption: "Drawing out knee pain." A man faces to the right, with his upper body straight and his legs bent at the knee.

12. Caption: "Drawing out swelling in the axillae (armpits)." A man wearing a cap and bowing his head walks with arms slightly lifted and hanging down from the elbows.

13. Caption: "Crane [lacuna]." A woman stands half turned to the right, with both arms raised and held out horizontally. (Therapeutic for the lungs.)

14. Caption illegible. A woman stands half turned to the right, with her head raised to the right. Her right arm is held diagonally up and to the front, and the left, diagonally down and to the rear. (To correct herniated disks.)

15. Caption: "Soaring dragon." A woman stands with arms splayed above her head, looking like a bird in flight. (Good for skin disease.)

17. Caption: "Stretching." This is the dōin "stretching bird" posture, except that the head is lifted.

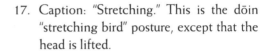

16. Caption: "Irritability and dizziness." A name for illness dating back to before the third century B.C.E. According to *Shih Chi* (*Records of the Historian*), this position is good for headache, fever, and irritability.

18. No caption. A man stands, but it is unclear what the accompanying movements are.

19. No caption. A partially clothed man stretches his right arm diagonally downward. The motion of his left arm is unclear.

21. Caption: "Looking up and calling." A man stands with his chest thrust out and both arms stretched behind him. Another pose assumed for promoting circulation of ki, this goes with diagram 20.

20. Caption illegible. A partially clothed man stands with his head bent forward and his eyes looking down. His arms are held slightly outward and to the sides, and his knees are slightly bent. This pose is assumed for promoting circulation of ki at the end of dōin practice.

22. Caption: "The monkey enjoys drawing off infection." The meaning refers to the commotion a monkey makes while washing itself. "Returning ki" is the cause of acute infectious disease. Considered in the context of diagram 15, a pose helpful in the case of skin disease, it appears that in ancient China infectious diseases were also treated with dōin. An obese, partially clad man stands with fists pointed downward and held to the sides of his abdomen. It is important to do this dōin exercise while constricting the anus. In my experience, this is effective against prolapsus.

23. Caption: "Drawing out fever." A man stands with wrists crossed above his forehead. The posture is said to be effective against burning or chills in the arms associated with fatigue, though I have not used it as such.

25. No caption. A partly clad man stands with left hand extended in front of him. The details are unclear.

24. Caption: "Sitting and drawing off the eight directions (corners?)" A partly clad man kneels with arms stretched diagonally front and back.

26. Caption: "Drawing out numbness." A partly clad man sits with both arms clasping his knees to his chest. A dōin pose effective for lower back pain.

27. A man stands slightly bent over, supporting himself with a staff held in both hands.

28. Caption: "Bear sniffs with paws on a tree." A man stands with both hands hugging the empty space in front of him. This is one of the "five animals" (tiger, bear, deer, monkey, and bird) exercises popular since before the Ch'in dynasty two millennia ago.

These diagrams on silk excavated at Mawangtui would seem to be the oldest extant explanations of dōin. The dōin techniques depicted therein are, of course, not identical with those practiced today, but they show an important developmental stage of the art. They also demonstrate how long dōin was practiced as a secret technique among the court aristocracy.

Dōin: The Art that Cures Diseases Baffling to Modern Science

Thanks to the many people who practiced and researched dōin, the art entered its mature stage during the Sui Dynasty in about 600 C.E. Its teachings were compiled in the *Treatise on the Causes of Disease* (*Chu Ping*

Yüan Hou Lun), the bible of dōin. Its importance to the art is equivalent to the *Treatise on Pain and Cold (Shang Han Lun)* for Chinese herb medicine or the *Inner Classic of the Yellow Emperor (Huang Ti Nei Ching)* for acupuncture, referred to earlier.

The author of the *Treatise on the Causes of Disease*, Ch'ao Yüan-fang, was appointed Grand Physician (T'ai Yi Po Shih) in 610. This would be the equivalent today of combining the positions of a minister of public welfare and the president of a national university of medicine. By imperial order, Ch'ao had a large number of people collect everything then known about dōin from all over China. The results, gathered over many years, were then assembled into his fifty-volume treatise.

The contents begin with detailed observations on the causes of disease, their external symptoms, and the characteristics reported by patients, together with curative measures, all of which involve dōin. The monumental work lists 1,720 names of diseases, including some familiar to us today, such as diseases of the heart and liver, abnormal blood pressure, cancer, diabetes, and psychological afflictions that would now be called neurosis or manic-depression.

Let us consider for a moment infection as a cause of illness. The treatise explains that according to where infection attacks the body and how long it takes for it to appear, symptoms and treatment will differ. For example, rheumatism enters the body via the groin area in winter, but it does not manifest itself until the following autumn. Dōin includes numerous methods that are unknown to most people today but are simple and effective to apply. These methods take immediate effect when the cause of the problem is accurately grasped.

The *Treatise on the Causes of Disease* has been translated from classical Chinese into the modern vernacular and is now used as a textbook in the school of Chinese medicine in T'aichung. Unfortunately, however, it is only treated as a dictionary of symptoms and pathology, and its important curative practices related to dōin are not included. The reason for this is that with the exception of certain Chinese Taoists, the dōin art in China has been completely forgotten. Regrettably, the dōin passages were excised because without knowing how to apply dōin in practice, the passages in the text related to the art were difficult to follow.

Dōin in Japan

Dōin came to Japan early. At the end of the fourth century C.E., during the reign of Emperor Ōjin, Chinese script (the future means of transcribing Japanese) was transmitted from the kingdom of Paekche, in what is now the Korean peninsula, when the Korean named Wani came to Japan bearing books. He is said to have brought the *Analects* (*Lun Yü*) of Confucius in ten volumes, the *Thousand Character Litany* (*Chien Tzu Wen*) in one volume, and *Study of the Calm Method* (*P'ing Fa Hsüeh*). The last includes explanations of martial arts and dōin. The *Study of the Calm Method* was later annotated by Sugawara Michizane (845–903), and thereafter passed on to the Murakami Genji and Seiwa Genji families. The book was transmitted actively through the generations by the Murakami Genji, experts at naval warfare, but it did not spread far beyond that house. One reason for its limited dissemination was the fact that the thought of Lao Tzu was difficult for Japanese to adopt and a Taoist priesthood was not generated.

But whereas the religious elements of Taoism did not thrive, its medical teachings in the form of dōin did. In the Edo period (1600–1868) dōin became central to Chinese herbal medical practice, and practitioners of the art appeared. One particularly well-known dōin practitioner was the haiku master Kamijima Onitsura (1661–1738). Onitsura had success curing disease through dōin techniques, and he made a good living treating three great lords.

After the Meiji Restoration of 1868, Western medicine was widely adopted and the new government actively suppressed Chinese herbal practices and native Japanese medical techniques. Dōin, too, despite its manifest successes, was forgotten by the majority of the population. Finally I alone was left to pass along the ancient dōin art. This came about because I am a lineal descendant of the Ōtakasa family, which in turn is a branch of the Murakami Genji, the original disseminators of dōin in Japan.

Let me now explain the relationship between my dōin teachings and the Lung Men school of Taoism. As I explained in the previous chapter, dōin began to disappear from mainstream society in China, beginning in about the seventh century. This phenomenon concurrently brought about the fragmentation of the teaching into various separate schools. Some incorporated herbal medicine, and others affiliated themselves with Buddhism or Confucianism. The Lung Men school was one of the strains that formed in this way. Before I became the head of the Lung Men lineage, I had become familiar with the practices of the Ōtakasa house and had investigated all the various dōin schools, reviving forgotten techniques and choosing between various practices in order to apply them most effectively to people living in the modern world.

The State of Dōin in Taiwan and China

After becoming the head of the Lung Men school, I again visited Taiwan in 1973 in order to participate in a meeting of the Taoists still remaining on the island. The purpose of the meeting was to introduce Taoist dōin and martial arts.

The Taoists invited by Mr. Chen were amazed as I demonstrated the arts of dōin and tao-kung ("merits accrued from the Tao," a martial-arts-related aiki-jutsu). Despite the fact that the dōin techniques I demonstrated were documented in ancient Chinese texts, they came as a complete surprise to the Chinese Taoists themselves for several reasons:

1. The Taoists had a tendency to sequester their doctrines and restrict the number of initiates.

2. Despite their small numbers, Taoist adepts were killed or repressed at the end of the Ch'ing Dynasty at the turn of the century.

3. Many ancient Taoist texts were lost in the social unrest at the end of the Ch'ing, with the result that few remained to be handed down to modern practitioners.

4. The limited number of texts that did remain were difficult to understand, being written in arcane or symbolic vocabulary.

The situation on the Chinese mainland was the same as in Taiwan. In the revolution of 1949, all the main Taoist practitioners fled abroad. Thirty years later, I received a request to attend an international conference from the city of Wen-t'eng in Shantung, the birthplace of the Lung Men school. I was welcomed as the only living practitioner of dōin and ch'i-kung (I will return to the latter art presently). Though the government of the People's Republic of China is working to collect and preserve as many of its traditional healing arts as possible, dōin is still relatively unknown. The version of the art that I teach is therefore much in demand among Chinese specialists. It was intro-

The author at international dōin conference in Shantung, China.

duced in China in an article that I presented in Japan, entitled "Ten Principles of Dōin, by Masao Hayashima, Head of the Nihon Dōkan," which was translated into Chinese and appeared in the professional journal of traditional medicine *Ch'i-kung tsa-chih*.

Energizing the Body

Let me now give some actual examples of the efficacy of the dōin method. On one occasion I received a sudden visit at the Nihon Dōkan from a dermatologist from the city of Nagoya. He related that he had applied dōin techniques learned from my book in the case of a twenty-eight-year-old woman suffering from facial discolorations. At first he had been somewhat skeptical of dōin, but he felt that since it was a completely benign technique, he would suggest that his patient try it out for two weeks and see if it helped. When she came back a week later, he was amazed at the results: the discolorations that had disfigured her entire face had already half disappeared.

The doctor also prescribed dōin techniques in the case of a forty-two-year-old woman who suffered from an itching sensation over her entire body. Since it had been determined that her blood pressure was high, the doctor prescribed dōin techniques to lower it. Before a week had passed, her blood pressure went down and the itching sensation disappeared.

Both patients had also suffered from fatigue, but both had resigned themselves to it, supposing it was simply the fault of their physical makeup. But after the dōin treatments, both indicated that they felt energy welling up from within, so that they awoke each morning feeling completely refreshed from the rigors of the previous day. The woman with facial blemishes had also been resigned to her condition, since her mother, grandmother, and great-grandmother had also suffered from them. And yet dōin was helpful there as well, and in a short period of time.

In all his years of medical practice, the physician had never seen such dramatic curative effects. He considered the dōin method to be truly wondrous, and he therefore had resolved to call on me and study it further.

But there is really nothing mysterious about the dōin method. All the functions of the body are interrelated. In the case of skin discolorations and blemishes, it is not only that the skin is at fault, but the internal organs as well. Given that, it is no surprise that fatigue should also occur. Dōin techniques focus on the body's interrelationships and adjust the flow of ki to recover health and vigor.

When the internal organs weaken, one becomes fatigued more easily, blemishes break out, the shoulder muscles tighten, and fat increases. The effects of alcohol also take longer to dissipate. These effects do not appear in a healthy person; they are all a kind of alarm bell that can result in more serious illnesses if ignored.

Obviously the nature of the symptoms varies from person to person, but the core reason for the loss of vitality is in all cases the same: a weakening of basic body function. If the causes for that decline can be removed, vitality will return. The type of dōin technique applied will differ according to the nature of the symptoms.

Using dōin techniques, I have seen large numbers of women become so youthful one wouldn't recognize them, and they have gone on to live long happy lives. And I have known numerous men who have lived into old age in joy and serenity, without a care in the world. These people, who bore their illnesses and worries alone before coming to Taoism, subsequently learned to make it central to their lives.

The cure of illness is only a stepping stone to the real goal of the dōin method. Those who do not attempt it will fail to understand its central features. As accustomed to Western medicine as we are, we tend to believe that it is enough simply if our illnesses are cured. But the dōin method aims not only to cure or prevent illness. What it strives for is the attainment of a completely free and unfettered quality of life. For example, if you relieve muscle tightness in the shoulders, you relieve tightness in the heart as well. In order to relax the heart, therefore, what dōin does, in essence, is to implement techniques to relax the shoulders. Those who feel that their shoulders are tight but their heart muscles are not should simply try the exercises to relax those shoulders. The proof of what I am saying will soon become clear.

For convenience, I have referred to dōin here as a health practice. But it is more accurate to say that it is a philosophical path toward the pursuit of a life of complete freedom.

THREE

BREATH, KI, AND DŌIN

The Taoist Road to Health

For as long as human beings have been on this earth, we have desired health and longevity. Some people reading this book may be devoted to jogging or to working out at the gym for those very reasons. But if you concentrate on training the body alone, you will never achieve true health. Countless numbers have died of heart attacks while jogging or have suffered back injuries from violent exercise. There is no quick and easy route to health maintenance. In traditional China, those who focused only on physical health through diet and exercise were derided. For a person to be completely well, he or she must have not only physical but spiritual health. The principle is called "Cultivating both the mind and the body." This is the true basis of youthfulness and longevity.

In ancient China, methods for rejuvenation and long life were developed and classified. The oldest is the art of dōin. As the centuries passed, shao lin ssu boxing, t'ai ki ch'üan, and pa tuan chin ("eight lengths of brocade") branched off from it. The latter two were revered as health practices among courtiers of the Ch'ing dynasty, and all continue to be employed.

The term dōin (tao-yin) means "guide and draw," that is, to guide ki and draw it into the body. The essence of the art is the drawing in of ki (in a word, breathing) and conducting it to every internal point. Other important aspects of the dōin art are concentration and relaxation. By concentration, I mean nothing more than, for instance, when doing an exercise for sore shoulders, focusing on the fact that by doing the exercise, your shoulders will get better. Relaxation refers to doing each exercise slowly and deliberately, then after it is finished, pausing for a few moments. It is then that the harmful ki is drawn out and the body heals. The widest meaning of the term dōin, then, is to live at all times in proportion and in harmony with nature.

The author responding to questions from audience at Nihon Dōkan.

When the dōin diagrams were discovered at Mawangtui in 1973, the art was suddenly thrust into the public eye. But actually it had never been lost, its secrets being handed down in the Taoist community. Its definition even appears in a dictionary long used in modern Japan, *Kōjien*: "A Taoist technique for curing and cultivating the body, based on stretching and moving the joints and limbs, meditation, massage, and breath control. A technique for longevity."

The reason that I have written this book is not only to explain the benefits of dōin but also to describe the Taoist world that gave rise to the dōin art.

What Is Ki?

I indicated earlier that the essence of dōin is to follow nature. The element that enables us to live our lives according to nature's rhythm is ki. Let us now discuss ki in more depth.

Below the navel is an area called the "cinnabar field," which Taoist belief holds to be the center of the body and the source from which ki emanates. Some people today equate the cinnabar field with the solar plexus, and view ki as a kind of lymph that circulates through the nervous system. While it is admittedly difficult to explain the nature and function of ki, I myself experience it on a spiritual plane. In general, I believe it can be conceptualized as air.

If deprived of air for three minutes, humans and animals suffocate. Modern science explains that when we breathe, we introduce oxygen into the body via the lungs. That oxygen bonds with hemoglobin in the blood and travels to every part of the body, producing energy. The carbon dioxide created in that process is then expelled during exhalation. That is the breathing process.

If ki is air, and if dōin deals with the way ki is manipulated, some people are erroneously led to conclude that ki is nothing more than oxygen. And yet it is important to remember that ki is not oxygen but an essence in its own right. Ki is air, ki is atmosphere, and at the same time it is a concept for hypothesizing nature and the universe.

Ki also flows, floats, and stagnates. It can be clear or turbid, hot or cold, violent or serene. Of particular concern is how ki moves through the body. Stagnant ki is not made to flow normally, and turbid ki must be dispelled from the system. At the same time, pure ki must be delivered throughout.

The Human Body: An Antenna for Ki

I understand that during the last decade, there has been in China a surge of interest in ch'i-kung therapy. The name ch'i-kung ("breath merit") is modern, but its therapeutic effects are generated by increasing circulation of ch'i (ki). It is, in fact, a medical practice based on dōin concepts. Chinese hospitals apparently include a department of ch'i-kung, staffed by physicians trained in ch'i-kung techniques. Among these physicians—one might call them "doctors of ki"—are some whom I hear are more popular than physicians trained in Western techniques. This is certainly appropriate to China, where the concept of ki was born.

The notion of ki was generated from among Taoists, who studied the teachings of the Yellow Emperor and Lao Tzu, and their secrets were generally passed down from master to disciple, and strictly kept from outside eyes. After the introduction of socialism to China, religion was suppressed, and what had theretofore been Taoist secrets were classified and studied in a more thoroughgoing scholarly manner. This in fact instituted a rebirth of the ancient Taoist secret arts and eremitic recipes for rejuvenation and longevity.

The new interest in ch'i-kung is proof of the renewed recognition of the function of ki in the body. There is a flow of ki between practitioner and patient, which prompts the patient's healing and recovery. In fact, diseases thought to be intractable are now being cured by ch'i-kung techniques. In a word, the body is an antenna for ki, and when waves of ki from outside are tuned to the same frequency as the ki in the body, the affected area is cured, as when flawed television reception suddenly becomes clear.

The basis of the medical techniques of ch'i-kung is tao-yin (dōin), and I have many patients who come to my dōin center when other physicians have given up on them. Several years ago, a mother arrived with a baby in her arms complaining of abnormalities in some of the fingers of the baby's left hand and asking if there was nothing that could be done to correct the problem. Sure enough, the three fingers between the infant's thumb and pinky were abnormally short. Tears came to her eyes as she related how she had taken the baby from clinic to clinic without success. As I examined the infant and talked with the mother, I determined that the problem could be cured. Since it is the fundamental premise of the art of dōin that you can cure disease by yourself, I resolved to use dōin to stimulate the baby's own curative powers. But this would be impossible without the mother's help. I therefore taught her various dōin techniques that she could apply with a mother's tenderness on her own child. Within two months the three stunted fingers had become perfectly normal.

The dōin method and ch'i-kung possess immense curative powers, but they function through the body's own antenna-like ability to receive ki. The problem, then, is the quality of each body's antenna. In actuality, ki is always radiating from our bodies. When we press our hand against a pain, it is because we instinctively know that ki radiates from the palm.

In 1978 a theory was published in China to the effect that the ki which emanates from the palms is infrared radiation. It was reported that infrared waves of nine microns were easily absorbed into the body and penetrated to its core. Today infrared therapy is used in numerous ways in modern medicine.

There is another scientific theory that the ki emanating from the palms is a kind of enzyme. If so, then it is no wonder that ki can cure disease. Enzymes are produced inside the body, but when they are artificially applied to the exterior, they activate inner vitality. This is easily demonstrated by planting flowers in two vases. Place your hands over one vase every day, so that your ki emanates into it. The flowers in that vase will grow quicker, their color will be better, and they will last longer.

A third theory holds that ki is a kind of human electromagnetism. Fishes like eels and catfish can generate enough electricity to stun even an ox or a horse. Humans too may be similar, and scientists in the former Soviet Union and the United States are investigating the electrical currents in the body. Electroencephalographs and electrocardiographs, used respectively to monitor brain and heart function, can measure the faint electrical impulses the body generates, and it seems fair to assume that there is something in the body that generates an electricity one might call "vital ki."

According to Professor Sasaki Shigemi of the University of Electro-Communications, ki is comparable to what is called zero-point energy in quantum mechanics. This refers to the faint energy detected in an environment that according to present laws of physics should not exist. The following experiment was undertaken. Tap water was boiled, then the water vapor was cooled to make an ionized distillate, through which electricity passes more easily. A ch'i-kung master, whose art involves being able to direct ch'i (ki), introduced ki into the distilled water. Using the healing power inherent in the hands, he stood a short distance from the water and held out his hands, imbuing it with ki. This ki-filled water had less electrical resistance than water with none, but the pH was the same, meaning that the ions in the water remained unchanged. The change in resistance, however, means that a change had ocurred in the water through the influence of ki energy. Ki had clearly had an effect. In this way the existence of ki, which had been determined through the highly developed powers of the philosophers of ancient China, was now isolated through modern scientific techniques.

Next let me introduce an interesting theory involving ki and breath. The Nobel Laureate Yukawa Hideki derived his success in particle physics in part through a hint from these lines from the T'ang poet Li Po, which epitomize Taoist thought:

> *Heaven and earth are the lodging of ten thousand things;*
> *The passing days and months are the transient travelers of a hundred ages.*

Dr. Seki Hideo, formerly professor at Tōkai University, pursued this line of inquiry and established a theory, inspired by his research on electronics and electronic communication, in which "dark particles" are the central feature. According to researchers in the natural sciences, subatomic particles combine to form atoms, which then further combine to form molecules, and thence to form compounds. Organic and inorganic matter are both comprised of atoms. Even light and force can be construed in this manner. In short, science as now constituted conceives of all natural phenomena in terms of elementary particles. Professor Seki, however, theorizes that subatomic dark particles twenty decimal places smaller than the atom constitute the basis of matter. These dark particles are smaller than electrons and so pass between electrons and the nucleus of an atom with ease. He believes these particles can be construed to be what has in the Asian world been heretofore labeled ki. "When we breathe," suggests Professor Seki, "what we are really doing is taking dark particles into the body and accessing the information they carry."

The Basis of All Arts and Skills: Breath

In ancient China, breath was considered the essential principle in gathering ki and causing it to circulate. In China, therefore, various breathing techniques have been developed over the centuries. But these techniques were never collected or systematized due to the traditions of secrecy in the various sects that generated them. In Japan, on the other hand, breathing techniques were developed and taught which were meant to be used in tandem with techniques for walking. The chronicle of a major figure in the world of nō drama recalls his impression of the ambulation techniques he received as a child as follows: "When I was taught the principles of walking and of breathing, I realized how close they were to those in nō drama. The essence of ambulation techniques is to induct air into the cinnabar field below the navel (see p. 72). Breaths are classified into three types (large, medium, and small) and from there into about one hundred smaller divisions." The most important point of his remarks concerned bringing air into the cinnabar field.

I have been emphasizing the fact that breath techniques are the fundament of the dōin method; it is now clear that those same techniques are central to ambulation techniques. And they are not limited to ambulation—Japanese dance, the tea ceremony, flower arranging, kabuki, and in fact all the arts require correct breathing technique. The same is true for martial arts—jūjutsu (the forerunner of jūdō) with bare hands, bōjutsu with a staff, kenjutsu (the forerunner of kendō) with a sword—none can be mastered without correct breathing.

It was natural for Taoists pursuing the concept of ki to develop such techniques. There are four basic types for the induction of ki: while reclining, while seated, while standing, and while walking. I will limit myself below to the first two.

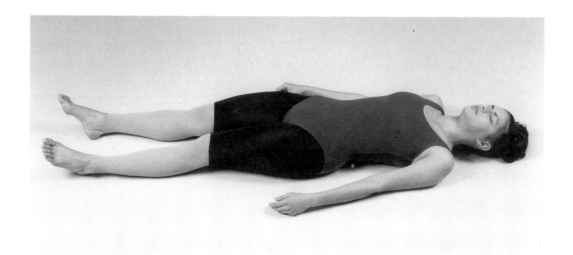

Lie down and exhale deeply through the mouth, naturally. When you finish exhaling, inhale naturally through the nose.

I. Breathing Technique While Reclining

One can think of this type of breathing as analogous to that performed by a healthy baby that is lying down.

1. Lie down and breath deeply. Always naturally, never forced. Exhale through the mouth.

2. When you finish exhaling, you naturally begin to inhale again. Do so through the nose, but without concentrating on the fact of breathing. In the beginning you may not notice, but as you proceed, your abdomen will begin to rise and fall. This shows that most of the time people use only half of their lungs to breathe.

   When you are breathing naturally, you will be filling your lungs completely with air and fully exhaling.

3. When you are able to breathe naturally, you will then learn to listen to your own breath. This is called *chōsoku* or "listening to the breath." But this does not mean concentrating all one's nerves on listening, but rather continuing to breath naturally. This means that even if your breathing loses cadence momentarily or is disrupted, you don't consciously adjust it, but rather let it naturally return to its own rhythm.

   As you perform this breathing technique, your mind will clear itself of its miscellaneous thoughts and ki will accumulate in your abdomen. If you pay attention, there are times when you will notice that your abdomen grows slightly warm.

II. Breathing Technique in Seated Meditation: Transferring into Your Body the Ki of the Universe

Those who have sat in Zen meditation (zazen) are already familiar with its ideal state of "nothingness" or "emptiness" (mu). But arriving at that state is immensely difficult. During meditation, countless conscious thoughts intrude. Among the challenging techniques for approaching mu, sitting in Zen meditation is the easiest. Thoughts that arise are simply allowed to float in the practitioner's consciousness; one need not chase them out or try to extinguish them. But if one begins zazen with a conscious attempt to achieve something concrete, like curing illness or earning money, one will fail. Instead, one must think of nothing at all, becoming like the air inside a vase, to attain the nothingness state.

This is also the ideal of dōin meditation. Anyone can perform the technique and enjoy its benefits, among which are the following:

1. Curing disease (if one has symptoms such as spinal pain, a heaviness in the head, or difficulty breathing, one first addresses the physical manifestation of the illness through other dōin practices, then begins meditation).

2. Relieving nervous anxiety

3. Anticipating danger

4. Foreseeing the future

All these benefits derive from harnessing into one's own body the ki of the universe.

Let us first consider the sitting technique of *banza*, also called *kekka-*

The seated breathing technique for increasing energy

Sit with your back straight and your eyes open only enough to let in a small amount of light. Clasp your hands in the *chikki* manner: the fingers of the right hand are held straight out, save for the middle finger (between the index and ring fingers) which is bent under the thumb. The left hand grasps the right hand from above, with the left thumb encircled by the thumb and bent middle finger of the right (see illustration on following page). The legs are in tanbanza position, used when banza is too difficult.

The full banza position, with feet resting on either thigh.

The *chikki* hand clasp used in seated meditation

fuza. The "ka" of the latter term refers to the inside of the foot, and the "fu" refers to the outside. Bend the right leg and place it on the left thigh. Next, take the left leg, draw it past the right knee, and rest it on the right thigh. The soles of both feet face upward. Banza means to sit like a great, still stone. Another term for this method of sitting is *sōban-fuza*. It is hard at first to become used to, and many cannot accomplish it. But it becomes natural with practice. For those who cannot reach that point, there is a modified posture, in which one simply places one leg on the thigh of the other leg bent beneath. This simpler technique is called *tanbanza*. Always breathe naturally.

As you sit in this posture, your various thoughts will fade away and ki will accumulate in your abdomen. Note that your abdomen may begin to feel warm.

One form of seated posture uses the *chikki* hand grip, in which one makes a circle with the thumb and middle finger of the right hand then grasps the right hand in the left, with the left thumb inserted in the circle made by the right down to the level of the ring finger. The sitter rests both hands below the navel. Take care not to rest the hands on your lap since this causes tension in the shoulders. Close your eyelids, but not entirely; keep them open enough for a sliver of light to enter. The mouth is firmly closed, with teeth together and the tongue lightly touching the upper gums. When you have rid yourself of mental static, focused your spirit, and reached quietude, then concentrate your vitality, ki, and spirit into the cinnabar field below your navel and continue thus from five to twenty minutes. Ki is the source of life and death; vitality is sexual energy, and spirit is, for example, the operation of the mind in the dream state.

Relaxing the Chain of Command from the Brain and Harmonizing the Internal Organs

The essence of this technique of quiet, seated meditation is to "listen to the ki" that you breathe. This doesn't involve any particular technique; you simply sit in meditation and focus your senses on apprehending ki. But this does not mean straining all your nerves, or concentrating on your nose and lungs, or listening to the sound the air makes as you breathe. It means instead to be aware of each cycle of inhalation and exhalation, without simply letting them become automatic.

This form of seated mediation involves quietude, in that it temporarily relaxes the chain of command from the brain, but it also includes action, in that it harmonizes the internal organs. The method of holding the hands and listening to breathing are not mentioned in other health practices; the chikki hand grip in particular has hitherto been secret.

But there are certain cautionary points to which one should pay attention:

1. Should you feel pain in the spine, heaviness in the head, difficulty breathing, or other physiological discomfort, stop meditating and only resume after it stops.

2. Sometimes during meditation the body will spontaneously begin to shake. This is called the *shindō* phenomenon, and some hold it to be healthful. I on the other hand believe it can have deleterious effects and so counsel immediate cessation of meditation should it occur.

3. When you begin meditation, you may be surprised at effects you don't normally notice, such as quick breaths or breaths of varying length. Do not try consciously to lengthen your breathing or make it regular; simply rely on your natural rhythms.

Some people naturally breathe shallowly and deeply in turns; there is no reason to artificially attempt to regularize the process. Simply leave the pace and depth of breathing up to nature. Those with knowledge of Zen may link this breathing practice to that of zazen, or they may feel that they must work to breath deeply from the abdomen, but there is no need to do either. This too involves focusing the thinking, which is inimical to the type of seated mediation described here.

As you sink deeper into the meditative state, you will find your mental static clearing, to the point where you achieve a complete wholeness of being. When you reach this point, you will also become oblivious to your breathing function. This is called the state of no-self. If when you reach this state you feel yourself growing sleepy, it is perfectly all right to stop meditating, stretch out, and go to sleep. There is no need to fight it. When you awake, your stress and anxieties will have vanished. Numerous examples have shown that seated meditation is also useful in cases of manic-depression.

I would like now to look a little more deeply into the concepts of "vitality," "ki," and "spirit," introduced earlier. These three elements must be completely realized for a person to live a healthy life. "Vitality," again, refers to sexual energy. Most people wrongly think that

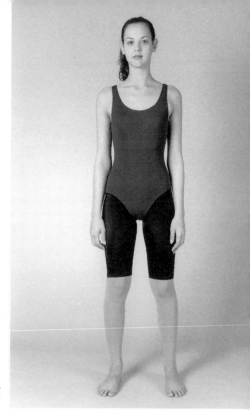

Standing perfectly straight, swing arms back and forth in parallel.

this refers to the sex act itself. Vitality does involve that, of course, but it also refers in a larger way to the life force as a totality. "Ki" is the inherent fundamental power with which people are imbued at birth. Internal ki accesses external ki and circulates it through the body. When ki is fully realized in the body, it becomes vitality, and vitality, for its part, may once again become ki. "Spirit" too is produced when ki circulates through the body in sufficient quality. Spirit, then, is predicated on ki. In modern terms, one might call spirit "rationality" or "intelligence." When humans lose this faculty, they are nothing more than animals, which function on vitality and ki alone.

The dōin method, then, rids the body of disease and promotes vitality and ki, and then on the basis of that, spirit as well. In this way the Taoist thought of Lao Tzu and the Yellow Emperor, which bonds humankind with the universe, constitutes a superlatively effective health regimen.

Swaiso: Driving Out Harmful Ki through Arm Movement

Another beneficial healing technique is swaiso (lit. "swing arms"), which is popular in modern China. In simple terms, swaiso involves waving the arms back and forth to shake off harmful ki. This harmful ki is the source of hardening, stiffness, tightness of the chest, and all

forms of disease. It is the purpose of swaiso to shake off harmful ki and sever its connections with disease in the body.

As I have said before, the fundamental goal of the dōin method is to drive harmful ki out, restore the flow of ki to all parts of the body, and let blood and lymph circulate normally again. Swaiso is one means to accomplish this goal.

A Simple Exercise

Swaiso is amazingly simple. I will explain the movements in order:

1. First, stand perfectly straight, feet planted firmly and separated by the width of your shoulders. Press down with your toes, as if to push them into the ground.

2. Next, swing both arms back and forth, in parallel. When you swing them backward, use a bit of force. And when you swing them forward, don't use any force; simply let momentum carry them out. When you start the swing, let your palms face downward. Keep your elbows perfectly straight. Look straight ahead, and avoid letting your attention stray. Count the number of swings to yourself, not out loud.

3. Beginners should swing their arms two to three hundred times, then gradually build up from there to an ideal of one or two thousand times, which can take about thirty minutes.

Ridding the Upper Body of Stiffness and Tightness

All of the body's internal organs are located in the upper body; the lower body includes simply the buttocks and the legs. The upper body, therefore, does most of the work, and it is the upper body that we are the more conscious of. Put a different way, in our daily lives our upper bodies are generally "full," and our lower ones are "empty." If, for example, you read non-stop for eight hours or more, the eyes become red, the head heavy, and the mind exhausted. What has happened is that the head had become overly full, relative to the rest of the body. This is a source of fatigue and illness. The entire upper body can develop this sense of heaviness and fullness, which then makes the lower body feel correspondingly "empty." When this condition persists over a long period, fatigue accumulates and various illnesses result due to a build-up of harmful ki.

The purpose of swaiso is to change the equation "upper, full; lower empty" to "upper, empty; lower full." In so doing, you rid your body of bad ki and the accompanying stiffness and tightness in the upper body and let fresh ki flow normally throughout. In order to effect this, you stand with your feet spread as wide as your shoulders and carry out the exercise with your muscles loose, your movements gentle, and your mind concentrated on your fingertips as your arms swing back and forth like a pendulum. Reach the point where you do this a thousand times each day.

The most important point is to make sure that you put seventy percent of your power into the lower body and only thirty percent into the upper. This is the main way to turn "upper, full; lower, empty" to "upper, empty; lower, full." Gradually the upper body will be relaxed and the lower will become strong and healthy. Even chronic illnesses will then disappear.

Relaxing the Upper Body and Lowering the Center of Gravity

But achieving the ratio of seventy to thirty is not easy. It is important to keep in mind the following main points:

1. Let your strength drain from your upper body. Keep your shoulders loose, and swing your arms naturally.

2. Keep your center of gravity in your lower body. This is the necessary concomitant to point 1. To effect this, keep the soles of your feet planted firmly on the ground. Be sure to do the exercise barefoot, without even socks.

3. Try to feel like your head is floating, suspended from above. This is good for relaxing the shoulders.

4. Keep the muscles of your mouth loose. Your mouth needn't fall open, but don't grit your teeth or clench your jaw muscles.

5. Try to rid your mind of miscellaneous thoughts. This too is to help empty the upper body.

6. Stand with your back straight.

7. Make your pelvis the axis of movement.

8. Do not raise your elbows too high.

9. Let your arms hang free.

10. Imagine that your arms are oars and that you are rowing the air.

11. Concentrate some of your energy into your cinnabar field, a spot normally construed as three inches below the navel, but actually three inches behind the navel into the interior of the

body. You can simply think of this strategic spot in Taoist medicine as the lower abdomen, and you should concentrate on that area as you exercise.

12. Do not constrict your inner thighs. Even though you are gathering your energy into your lower body, you should not go so far as to make your thighs tense.

13. Try to keep the anus at a 90 degree angle to the floor.

14. Imagine that your heels are heavy stones—keep them firmly on the ground.

15. Press your toes downward as if to bite into the ground below them.

16. As you swing your arms, make sure your palms face down.

Make Your Legs Great Trees that Sink Their Roots into the Earth

Among the above sixteen points are several hints to achieve the thirty-seventy ratio you need to achieve the "upper, empty; lower, full" ideal. Let us examine them in more detail.

When you swing your arms back, make your feet the center of gravity. Stand as if your legs were ancient trees whose roots sink into the earth, or as if they were stakes driven deep into the ground. Since there are meridians running from the soles of the feet, this kind of stance works to massage the ki-rich blood in that area. The beneficial effects of this spread out to the muscles, skin, and bones of the entire body.

A common mistake is to think that since swaiso is an exercise involving the arms, the legs can be neglected. But if the legs are allowed

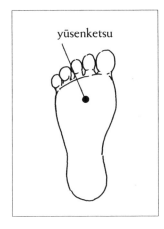

yūsenketsu

A particularly important
tsubo in soles of feet.

to relax, then you will revert to "upper full, lower empty," and the exercise will be worthless. Since the exercise is one of swinging the arms, most people forget the legs and the pelvic area. The exercise may be called "swaiso" (swinging arms), but in reality it is the legs and hips rather than the arms that are most important.

Particularly essential is an acupuncture point (tsubo) called the "bubbling spring point" (*yūsenketsu*) in the soles of the feet, which governs the operation of the kidneys. Heart palpitations, shortness of breath, and insomnia can be cured by massaging the bubbling spring point. The feet are a source for the cure of many diseases of the internal organs. Therefore concentrating your strength into your feet is a way to restore equilibrium to your ki blood and overcome those illnesses.

As you practice swaiso, you will feel tightness in the chest and abdomen disappear and a sense of well-being develop. Both feet will grow warm as blood begins to reach places where it had not previously been circulating effectively. When this happens, it is proof that ki-rich blood, the main focus of swaiso, is flowing unimpeded.

This is also the greatest effect of dōin as a health technique. It is for that reason that the dōin method is seen as the most important of Chinese health systems. When you exercise the arms and legs during swaiso, the muscles of the back, chest, and abdomen are naturally called into play. This in turn breaks down the impediments to the circulation of ki blood and reduces the amount of tired blood. The meridians too return to their normal function.

Among the diseases most frequently cured by swaiso are high or low blood pressure, cirrhosis of the liver, and arthritis. Most of the rheumatism patients who come to Nihon Dōkan have suffered from the disease for over ten years, have suffered crippling of the hands or legs, and have been abandoned by practitioners of conventional medicine. If you too have suffered from arthritis for no more than three or four years and are still at the point where fluid is building up in the right hand one day and the left the next, then swaiso can help. If swaiso does not improve your condition, it means that the disease has been allowed to progress too far, in which case one of the more specialized exercises should be employed instead.

FOUR

CURING CHRONIC
ILLNESS

The Art of Dōin: Fifteen Points

There are fifteen points that are central to the practice of dōin. This may sound like a large number, but those fifteen can be broken down into four categories: breathing; before beginning the dōin exercise; during the exercise; and concluding the exercise. All are simple and easily remembered.

Quite a few people are careful in the beginning to follow the rules closely but then, as they grow used to the methods, feel that they can cut corners occasionally. But these fifteen rules are all essential for increasing the effectiveness of the art, and each one should be observed every time without fail.

Breathing

1. Always inhale through the nose and exhale through the mouth. Close your mouth when you inhale. In order to introduce fresh ki as fully as possible throughout your system, exhale all the air in your lungs. Doing so will naturally ensure the circulation of air when you inhale again.

2. When you regulate your breathing to your physical movement, time your exhalation so as to finish it at the same time that you finish the movement.

3. The movements that you do to accompany your breathing should be done as a rule with your eyes closed. But there are also a few that are practiced with your eyes open, and in those cases, follow the specific accompanying directions.

Most people think of breathing as something done unconsciously and with no special effort. That is a great mistake. Many modern people breathe incorrectly, and that is a cause of dysfunction and disease. Always concentrate on following the rules correctly. It bears repeating that the special effects of dōin that make it uniquely effective among medical practices are based on correct breathing in conjunction with appropriate physical movements.

Before Beginning a Dōin Exercise

4. Open a window and fill the room with fresh air. If possible, leave the window open when you do the exercises, but in the winter it is best to close it and keep the room warm.

5. Wear clothing that does not confine the body or impede freedom of movement. You can even do the exercises in your pajamas or in your underwear. Remove all accessories such as necklaces, watches, glasses, or contact lenses. Perform the exercises in your bare feet, not in your socks.

6. Do the exercises on an empty stomach. Wait at least two hours after eating before beginning. And do not do the exercises more than three times a day.

7. Wait for the effects of alcohol to dissipate before beginning.

8. After bathing, wait at least ten minutes for your body temperature to return to normal before beginning.

Numbers four and five are essential for expelling the harmful ki that has accumulated in the body. Tight clothing impedes circulation as well as the expulsion of harmful ki. Since this unhealthy ki is expelled in particular from the soles of the feet, it is necessary to perform the exercises in bare feet only.

Numbers six and seven are related to the time you exercise. Choose the time of day that is most convenient. Often the easiest time is when you have just awoken, for you can perform some of the exercises in bed.

During a Dōin Exercise

9. First close your eyes (except in certain cases indicated by specific directions), relax your shoulder muscles, and let your mind find its natural equilibrium.

10. Next, breath out completely to rid your body of harmful ki. This must be done once at the very least. Then begin the various exercises.

11. Do not go to extremes in your exercises. Doing them only as long as they feel good is the way to cure dysfunction and disease. For example, if you can't carry out the recommended number of repetitions, it is all right to do only the number you feel comfortable with.

12. Those exercises involving massage of a part of the body should be done after you have rubbed your palms together to warm them. In the winter, you may want to warm your hands over the stove. In addition, you should massage the skin directly, not through clothing. Rub four or five times so that the spot grows warm. Don't do this in a perfunctory manner, but out of a desire to make your body better.

Numbers nine and ten should be followed for every exercise. Of course, it is perfectly all right not to stop at one exercise but to combine several, according to your symptoms.

Concluding a Dōin Exercise

13. Wipe off perspiration with a dry towel after you exercise. Since harmful ki exits via the soles of the feet and the nape of the neck, cleanse those areas with a moist wash cloth.

14. Do not immediately take a bath after the exercises, as that will dissipate their beneficial effects. Wait at least thirty minutes.

15. For those who have recently undergone surgery, different exercises may be prescribed.

The last point is particularly critical and is dangerous to ignore.

While taking a deep breath, raise your shoulders to the point where your neck disappears.

Exhale while letting your shoulders drop back down.

Sore Shoulders

I used to think that sore shoulders was the curse of only older people, but I find that recently even elementary school children suffer from it. When you figure in the number of people who are not even aware they suffer from it, the total reaches staggering proportions. One might think that shoulder soreness is rather low on the list of health priorities, but actually it is often linked to fatigue in the internal organs. There are cases in which a patient complaining of very sore shoulders has been diagnosed with liver trouble, for example.

Chronic pain is not something that will be completely cured by massage. Instead it should be dealt with in the early stages by applying dōin to improve the circulation of ki-rich blood and by excising harmful ki from the shoulders. To do this, I prescribe an exercise you can do even at the office: dropping the shoulders.

1. You can perform this exercise seated in a chair, but in the morning and evening at home you should sit in the banza or tanbanza position. Let your arms hang by your sides.

2. Exhale completely, then hunch up your shoulders as far as they will go. While raising your shoulders, inhale through your nose.

3. Then completely relax your shoulders and let them drop back down, exhaling through your mouth at the same time. Do this nine times.

Grasping hands behind head, breath in through nose.

Raising chin, breathe out slowly through mouth.

Bending head down, breathe in through nose.

Fatigue and Listlessness

It almost seems the loss of "get up and go" is endemic to the work place nowadays. Eighty or ninety percent complain of it. It may involve simple physical fatigue, but often mental fatigue or neurasthenia is manifest as well. Often it is the result of overburdening the liver. Diabetics are also easily fatigued.

I would like to introduce here the exercise called "opening the sides." This means to open up and dispel obstinate harmful ki built up in the sides of the body. This is effective in cases when you feel listless and tired even when you have not exerted yourself. It is good for diabetes, rheumatism, liver fatigue, anemia, muscle debilitation, and beriberi.

1. Sit in the banza or tanbanza position (or in a chair). Grasp your hands behind your head and breathe in through the nose.

2. Slowly but firmly raise your chin so that your neck bends back. As you do so, slowly breathe out harmful ki through your mouth.

3. When you have exhaled completely, bend your head downward while breathing in pure air through your nose and letting it permeate your body.

It is important to correlate your movements to your breathing. Do the entire exercise five to seven times.

Sitting with legs stretched out, hold your chin in left hand with right hand on the back of the head. While exhaling through mouth, use hands to move head slowly to the left.

"Middle–aged Shoulders"

People of middle age may suddenly find that it is difficult to raise their arms or that their shoulders hurt and refuse to move normally. These "middle-aged shoulders" appear anywhere from forty to seventy years of age. Western medicine sees this as a necessary evil of the aging process and does little more than prescribe tranquilizers or let nature take its course.

Middle-aged shoulders are simply the result of the accumulated effects of aging being concentrated in the shoulders. If you can expel the harmful ki from them, the shoulders will be cured. You first begin with the exercise for sore shoulders explained earlier. After you have done so, you may find that while the pain in the shoulders is gone, the oppressive feeling in the neck and head remains. If so, the discomfort can be alleviated in the following manner:

1. Sit with your legs out in front of you. As indicated in the illustration, rest your chin on your left hand and put your right hand on the back of your head.

2. While exhaling through your mouth, use your hands to move your head slowly to the left. Then with your mouth closed, return your head to its original position.

3. Then switch hands and move your head in the same way to the right. Do this in both directions three times. In this exercise, it is beneficial to keep your eyes open. Be careful not to move your shoulders. If you feel pain while moving your head, don't force it.

If you do this exercise three times a day (morning, noon, and night), you should regain freedom of motion in your neck by the third day, and by about the fifth day you should be able to raise your arms comfortably.

While exhaling from mouth, slowly bend over as far as you can. Then close the mouth and return to upright position.

Back Strain

Back strain may seem like something that suddenly happens one day, but actually that is not the case. There is always a long-term cause for those who complain of back strain, be it those who have unconsciously put a burden on their back through poor posture or through undue stress over a prolonged period, or those who have lately come to feel undefined back pain. When they happen to lift something heavy, for example, the weakened back is strained. It is essentially an accident waiting to happen. And once it does, it can be so severe that they can only stand ramrod straight, incapable of any motion at all. In such cases, dōin can be of great help.

1. Stand up straight, then while exhaling through the mouth, gently bend forward as far as you can.

2. Then close your mouth and return to your original upright position. As you continue this exercise, your flexibility will gradually improve to the point where you can touch both hands to the floor. When you achieve this, your back pain will have disappeared.

Sit on the floor and bend the legs so that the heels nearly touch the buttocks. Then hug knees to face. Hold this posture for two to three minutes.

Some people try to reach this point as soon as possible by bouncing lower and lower, and the exercise instead turns into some sort of sport and loses its curative power. You should go slowly and with patience—it only takes a total of two or three hours over a period of time until the back is cured, so there is no need to hurry or go overboard. Be careful not to bend your knees.

There is also a technique for avoiding back strain before it occurs. It is good for back pain as well. Sit on the floor and bend your legs so that your heels nearly touch your buttocks, then hug your knees to your face with your arms. Hold that posture for two or three minutes. You may breathe as you wish.

If you do this twice a day, your back pain will be gone in less than half a week. But this exercise is surprisingly difficult, so do not overextend yourself. Those with stomach or abdominal complaints should avoid it.

Constipation

There are huge numbers of people who feel that a carefully balanced daily diet is the best route to health. This is indeed effective in that it replenishes the body's ki. But no matter how full of ki the body is, that ki may go bad and become harmful if it is not effectively eliminated. In other words, excretion is just as important as intake for the maintenance of a healthy body, and you must pay attention to both.

For this reason it is best to attend to the problem of constipation as soon as it starts. One effective way to do this is to stimulate the stomach via abdominal massage. Constipation starts when the stomach and intestines stop functioning normally. If you begin to make it a practice to simply endure constipation, it will become habitual due to increasing gastrointestinal weakness.

Abdominal massage should be practiced as follows:

1. Lie on your back with your knees bent.

2. Lightly rub your entire abdomen twenty to thirty times with the palms of your hands. It is important that you massage the skin directly, not through clothing.

3. Mentally divide your abdominal area into a three by three point grid as in the illustration, then with your fingers together work your way from bottom to top, pressing each of the nine points with both hands. Each time you lift your fingers to go to the next point, gently exhale. If when pressing a point you encounter a lump, that is a stool concentration. If you massage that area, you may begin to feel a strong urge to evacuate.

If you do this exercise morning and evening on an empty stomach, your constipation will soon be cured. This technique has the added

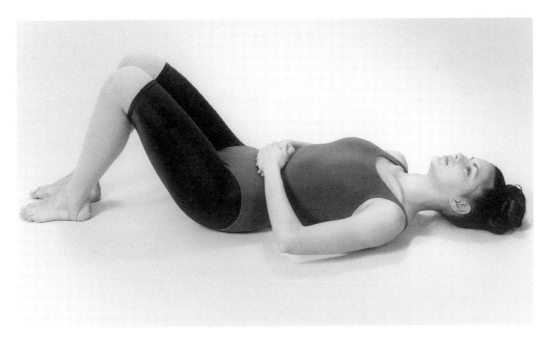

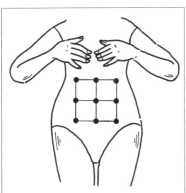

Lie on back with knees up, and lightly rub entire abdominal area. Press the points in the illustration at left from the bottom up with the fingers of both hands. If you encounter a lump, massage it.

benefit of getting rid of stool that has become fixed to the abdominal walls and given rise to complexion problems and menstrual cramps caused by the resultant harmful ki. Abdominal massage is traditionally counted as a secret technique for longevity and rejuvenation, and it can help prevent aging.

Those who have undergone abdominal surgery should absolutely refrain from step three above. They should simply rub the abdomen with the palm of the hand, avoiding strong pressure with the fingers.

Clasp your hands behind your head and bend your knees.

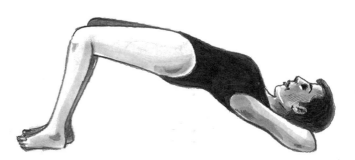

While exhaling softly, slowly raise your abdomen from the floor. Then when you have exhaled completely, close your mouth and softly return to your beginning posture.

Reducing Your Waistline

Food portions are growing, and with them, waistlines. This is a worry for women and middle-aged men in particular. Overeating is generally thought to be the cause, and many try to diet in response. But this is problematic from the point of view of dōin. The case of one young woman shows why. She tried limiting herself to one bowl of rice a day, and while she did lose weight, she also became anemic within a month. She had cut down on not only pounds but on strength.

Obesity results from the diminution of basic bodily functions and from the abnormal operation of the evacuatory organs. The real way to lose weight, therefore, is not to cut down on food but to restore elimination to normal. In so doing, you will reduce your weight and your waistline.

If you wish you may first apply the very fundamental abdominal massage technique on page 94 and then continue immediately with this one. Or you can do this exercise on its own.

1. Lie on your back with your knees up. Clasp your hands behind your head.

2. From this posture, raise your abdomen as in the illustration. It is important to gently exhale through the mouth as you do so. After you have exhaled completely, close your mouth and gently lower yourself back to the floor.

If you repeat this exercise three times daily, in about five days you will lose flesh appreciably around the waist. In a month men will find their belt sizes have decreased, and women will be more shapely.

This exercise is meant to stimulate bodily elimination. Through it, abdominal fat changes to fresh blood. Your abdomen may initially grow lined after losing weight, but don't worry—this will eventually disappear.

Sit with your eyes closed and exhale through mouth.

Breathe in through nose, then pinch nostrils closed with right hand.

Headache

There are many causes of headaches. The most common is sore shoulders, followed by constipation or empyema (the accumulation of purulent matter). In women, headaches are also caused by menstrual irregularities or other gynecological factors. The harmful ki built up by sore shoulders or by menstrual problems spreads throughout the body, and when it reaches the brain it impedes the function of the blood vessels, with a headache the result. In the case of constipation, the toxins from the stool spread throughout the body, and with empyema, purulent matter builds up not only in the nasal cavity but, in severe cases, even behind the eyes and forehead, again resulting in headache. This may not seem plausible to moderns, but I have seen it again and again in my experience as a health practitioner.

It would therefore make sense to treat headaches by going to their source, whether empyema, constipation, sore shoulders, or other causes. But there is also a more straightforward and immediate cure that I would like to introduce here.

Move eyes left and right as far as you can, until they start to tear.

When you need to breathe, remove hand from nose and exhale through the mouth.

1. Sit with your eyes closed and exhale slowly through the mouth.

2. Take a deep breath through your nose, then pinch your nostrils closed with your right hand.

3. While pinching your nose, look to the left without moving your head, then look to the right, in both cases moving your eyes to the sides as far as possible, so that your vision blurs and tears come to your eyes. You should look to the left for half the time you are holding your breath, and to the right for the other half.

4. When holding your breath starts to hurt, release your nose and exhale through your mouth.

If you do this five to seven times, your headache will disappear. It is also effective for temporary loss of hearing due to illness. If this doesn't work, try repeating the process two or three times. After your headache goes away, you may experience other surprising benefits, such as improvement in farsightedness.

Hair Loss and Graying

Hair loss and graying are often said to be hereditary. Many think that because their father went bald that they will too. Certainly heredity is a factor, which in dōin is expressed as a person's karma. If a person does not want to go bald, he should explore techniques that will undo the karma that causes it. Changing the karma inherited from one's ancestors may seem like an impossible task, but dōin practices can change anyone's. Harmful ki accumulates in the physically weak areas to which karma has predisposed the body.

For hair loss and graying, it is important to start a regimen to improve the circulation of blood rich in ki. As the bones age, the skin of the head develops irregularities, and as those places harden, graying, hair loss, and baldness can result. But if you practice dōin, you can prevent these from occurring. It is at once a preventative and a curative approach.

1. Sit with your legs stretched in front of you.

2. With the fingers of both hands, massage your scalp in an upward direction eighteen times.

3. With the palms of both hands, lightly pat your head eighteen times.

Do this twice a day, or five times or more if your condition is advanced. After one week you will begin to see curative improvements in hair loss and graying, and in ten days or so those experiencing balding should begin to sense changes. After two months increased hair growth will be apparent.

Baldness normally goes from the sides to the front to the middle, but the cure goes backwards, from the middle to the front to the sides.

With the fingers of both hands massage your head in an upward direction.

Lightly pat the head with the palms.

As the hair begins to grow in, it will feel dry or feathery to the touch.

Those with white hair may lose dozens of strands temporarily, but do not be concerned; the ones falling out are the weak ones, and the ones that grow back will be softer and darker.

Pollen Allergies and Rhinitis

When you inhale pollen, dust, or other allergens, the mucous membranes of the nostrils may experience an allergic reaction, resulting in allergic rhinitis (nasal inflammation) with constant sneezing and a runny nose. People with a tendency toward empyema are especially prone, and dōin medicine does not particularly distinguish between the two conditions.

Nasal problems can lead to loss of concentration and inability to work. But if you remove nasal matter through the following exercise, you will stop being troubled by nasal inflammation and avoid the possibility of surgery for empyema.

1. Massage the sides of your nose up and down with your middle fingers eighteen times or so to encourage the flow of matter.

2. Close your left nostril and scoop some water into your right palm. Then breath it in through your right nostril and spit it out through your mouth. It may be easier if, when you introduce the water to your nostril, you bend your head back.

3. Repeat for the right nostril.

Do this three times for each nostril in the morning and in the evening. There are cases in which matter will continue to drain for two or three months, but once you rid yourself of it, you will cure the complaint and your nostrils will be cleared. This practice may at first be quite uncomfortable for those unused to it. It is like trying to run water through a sooty chimney. But there is something you can do for this. In the beginning, try using lukewarm water. The matter clinging to your nostrils will dissolve without much discomfort and flow out. In

Massage both sides of your nose to loosen nasal matter.

Close your left nostril and scoop water into your right palm.

the beginning, the left nostril may be obstructed, and then perhaps the right one, and your voice may grow slightly nasal for a while, but after a week or two this will disappear, and the process will become easier. At that point you may start to use cold water instead of lukewarm.

Vision Loss

Nearsightedness doesn't seem to be normally considered an illness; many people put on thick glasses and consider themselves healthy. But on reflection this seems a bit odd—how can eyes that no longer see properly be considered normal?

The various kinds of vision problems, be they nearsightedness, farsightedness, presbyopia (aging vision), etc. are caused by deformities of the cervical vertebrae. Since this is indeed a dysfunction, it needs to be cured. Let me begin with one approach applicable to all forms of vision loss.

First immerse your face in a sink filled with water and blink your eyes. This in itself is beneficial in restoring vision and is also a form of protection against cataracts and glaucoma. Do it morning and night, and also for particular effect whenever you return home from an outside errand.

Those who wish to improve their vision even further can try the following exercise:

1. First warm your hands by rubbing them together, then lightly apply them to both eyes. Keep your eyes closed. You may do this either with your legs stretched out or while seated in a chair.

2. While covering your eyes, move them up and down three times, then left and right three times, then left and right again three times. Do this whole sequence three times at least.

The exercise should be done three times a day, morning, noon, and night. It replenishes the ocular blood supply and eliminates harmful ki in the form of liquid extruded from the tear ducts. Doing so is the route to the restoration of vision. If you carry out both these exer-

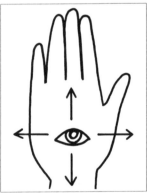

Rub your hands together, then lightly place them over your closed eyes. With your eyes closed and covered, move your eyes up and down, side to side, and again side to side three times each.

cises, you will find that farsightedness improves in five days, astigmatism in a week, and nearsightedness in two to three months. The cause of presbyopia is debilitation of the feet—for countermeasures see page 124 on athlete's foot and corns.

Insomnia

Insomnia is a very widespread affliction. Sometimes the cause is easily identifiable—overtiredness, for example, or toothache. But it is particularly troublesome when the cause can't be pinpointed. You may try to change your position in bed, or you may resort to alcohol, but nothing seems to help. You fret, and your body suffers as well.

There are also many who cannot get enough deep sleep. Most of these people dream a great deal. Since they are sleeping so lightly, they wake up at the slightest interruption.

Dōin is useful for these afflictions. Let me explain one exercise called "The Dragon's Sleep." It takes its name from the posture you assume while practicing it. Before closing your eyes for the night, do the following:

1. Remove your pillow and lie on your left side.

2. Rub your hands together to warm them, then place one over the other. Place the hands between the thighs. A man should then place them around the scrotum; women, around the pubic region.

There is no specific breathing exercise required. You will begin to feel more relaxed, and you should soon fall asleep. As you place your hands in the indicated area, bend your knees. For those who absolutely cannot sleep without a pillow, use as flat a one as possible.

You can fall asleep in as little as three minutes using this technique. Those who usually sleep lightly and dream frequently will instead benefit from deep and dreamless rest. And those who usually rise frequently during the night to urinate will find that such episodes decrease.

Lie on your left side. Rub hands to warm them, then press them together. Place the hands between the thighs. Women should then place them around the pubic region, and men around the scrotum.

If you continue this for a week, you will find that even if you awake in the night, your eyes will naturally fall shut again, and you will awake in the morning refreshed.

Kneel on one leg and grasp the upright knee with both hands.

As you draw the forehead to the knee, exhale.

High or Low Blood Pressure

High and low blood pressure are opposite phenomena, but they have the same fundamental cause—failure of blood to flow freely due to obstructions from vascular aging. When such obstructions develop, either high or low blood pressure will result according to the makeup of the individual. Doctors will prescribe relaxants for those with high blood pressure or boosters for those with low. But these are only quick fixes; they do not address the fundamental issues. The patient must take the drugs constantly.

Dōin, by contrast, addresses the basic problems by reinvigorating the aging blood vessels. It works as follows (see the illustration on p. 124 for athlete's foot and corns):

1. Stretch out one leg and place the other leg crossed over it.

2. Massage each toe, from big to small.

3. Next place the palm of the hand over all five toes and move them back and forth.

4. Apply pressure with both hands to the soles of the feet.

Do this to both feet. This technique is effective because the respiratory and circulatory organs are both connected to the fingers and toes. Do the exercise as long as time permits. If you can do it for an hour or two, you will find you blood pressure going back to normal that very day. Young people will be cured in two days, and older people in five.

It is also good to add this exercise as well:

1. Kneel on one leg and grasp the upright knee with both hands and draw the forehead to the knee.

2. When your head touches your knee, exhale and return your head to its original upright position while closing your mouth.

This technique will be most effective if you perform it three times a day.

Sit in the tanbanza posture and breathe once.

While inhaling through the nose, raise arms high above head.

Anemia

Anemia is caused by obstructions in blood circulation. It is not solely the result of an insufficiency in blood volume due to poor nutrition. This is why it frequently occurs in women when parts of the body are compressed by a brassiere or girdle. In the interest of slimming down, many women nowadays also go without breakfast, have a salad for lunch, and a very light dinner. Their blood grows thin and they lack energy. Anemic collapse is a natural outcome.

The first thing to do when anemia strikes is to loosen all garments that restrict the body so that it can relax. This in itself usually brings improvement in the symptoms. But dōin will build up the body so that it can deal with anemia's fundamental causes.

1. Sit in the banza or tanbanza posture gripping your thumbs inside your fists, and breathe in and out once.

2. While inhaling through the nose, raise both arms high above your head.

While holding breath, turn your head three times to the left as far as possible, then exhale. Inhale again and turn head three times to the right, then while exhaling through the mouth, lower arms.

3. Holding your breath, turn your head three times to the left and then exhale through the mouth.

4. Inhale again through your nose and then turn your head three times to the right, then while exhaling through your mouth, lower your arms.

Perform the entire exercise three times a day. In a week you may find that you no longer suffer from anemia. It is important to turn your head slowly and as far as possible. This is because the neck is not only the route through which the blood passes to the brain, but it also supports a significant part of the body's weight and can therefore age quickly under the strain. By turning the head slowly as far as possible, you keep it flexible and vigorous. This technique is meant to maintain the smooth circulation of ki in the upper body, but since it also prevents the neck from aging, it is very effective in protecting against other age-related diseases, like strokes.

Ringing in the Ears

After reaching fifty years of age, an increasing number of people start to suffer from ringing in the ears (tinnitus). Modern science speculates that the cause may be changes in lymphatic pressure or viral infection, but the real reason may simply lie in a failure over a long period to care for the ears. Many may insist that they are careful to clean their ears regularly and remove wax, but this is not true ear care. Until the harmful ki is completely driven from the ears and ki-rich blood is again circulating freely, symptoms such as a metallic ringing or a sibilance will not be cured.

It is not too late for even those who view tinnitus as an inevitable concomitant to aging to overcome the symptoms through proper ear care.

1. Sit with both legs stretched in front of you, grasp your ears with your index and middle fingers, and wiggle your ears up and down eighteen times.

2. Next insert your index fingers into your ears with a modicum of pressure. Hold them there for two or three seconds, then remove them. Repeat this three times, each time trying to make your ears pop when you remove your index fingers.

If you do both exercises twice a day for ten days, the ringing in your ears will completely disappear. If the symptoms reappear later, you can cure them by immediately applying the techniques again.

It is important to remember when rubbing the ears up and down to grasp them not by the earlobes but by the entire region surrounding the ears.

If you continue this for several days, your skin may become red

Grasp your ears with index and middle fingers and wiggle them up and down eighteen times.

Insert forefingers into ears, hold them there for two or three seconds, then remove them, popping ears in the process.

and sore, but that is because it has become weakened. If you stop for a while, it will return to normal.

Note too that many ear diseases are due to empyema. In these cases refer to the section on pollen allergies and rhinitis.

Bladder Infections

Bladder infections are more common in women than in men. One reason is postponing urination. As indicated earlier, for the same reason that constipation gives rise to harmful ki, so does postponing urination. In women, moreover, the urethra is shorter and wider than in men, and the distance between the urinary meatus and the anus is shorter. This makes it easier for bacteria to enter the system, during menstruation, for example. One way to prevent bladder infections is to keep this area clean. Such infections can also be caused by frequent sexual intercourse, or by intercourse when the woman is not ready.

To cure bladder infections, lie comfortably on your side or on your back. Rub your hands together to warm them, then press your palms over the groin or bladder area (located where the legs connect with the trunk). Massage directly as long as you like.

If you are lying on your side, massage the upper side of the bladder, then lie on your other side and massage the other side. Also, when you are lying on your side, it is important to adopt a position that is comfortable. Straighten the bottom leg and bend the upper one a bit. In this posture it is easy to stretch out your upper arm and massage the affected area.

Generally when people lie on their sides they bend both legs or at least the bottom one. But doing so curves the spine and reduces the beneficial effects of this exercise. Therefore make sure that you use the correct posture outlined here.

This technique has very quick results. If you employ it for an hour a day, most people find that in three to four days both chronic and acute bladder infections disappear.

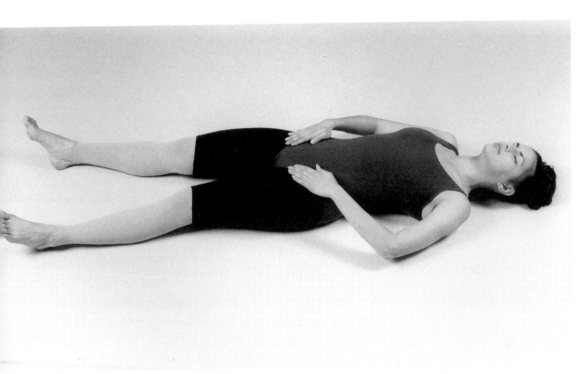

Lie comfortably on back, and after rubbing your palms together to warm them, massage both sides of the bladder as long as you like.

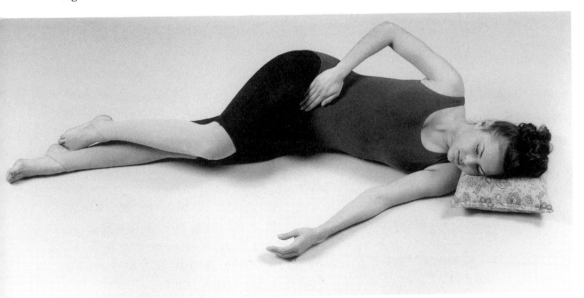

If you choose to lie on your side, massage the top side of the bladder first, then lie on the opposite side and massage the other side.

Hemorrhoids

Hemorrhoids develop because of harmful ki accumulating due to poor circulation and congestion in the anal region. Congestion is apt to be caused by certain postures, such as sitting too long in a chair or squatting. People who drive motor vehicles for a living or sit all day in an office are particularly vulnerable. Men are more likely to suffer from the disease than women, but women who are pregnant or who sit a great deal at home are also susceptible. Particularly in the case of women, hemorrhoids left untreated can lead to loss of one's figure. It is not a disease to be taken lightly.

In order to cure or prevent hemorrhoids, the most important point is to avoid congestion in the anal region. Avoid lengthy pressure on the area, cold, and constipation. Also alcohol or other stimulants taken in excess cause congestion of the mucous membranes, and that is to be avoided as well.

The dōin approach to treating hemorrhoids will be ineffective if the above preventative measures are ignored. The main point in the treatment is to stimulate the flow of blood in the buttocks and rid the anal region of congestion.

1. Stand with your legs slightly apart (about the width of your shoulders).

2. Place the thick of the ring finger and little finger on the split between your buttocks and move the fingers up and down in a vibrating motion for one minute.

3. Repeat using the other hand.

Alternate hands five times each, for a total of ten minutes, two or

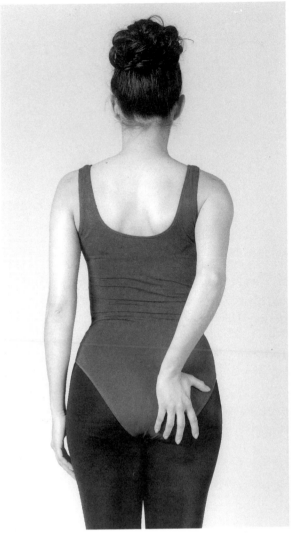

Place the thick of your ring finger and little finger on the split between your buttocks and vibrate your fingers up and down for one minute.

three times a day. Do this in the bathroom after you have had a bowel movement. In the case of minor hemorrhoids, bleeding will stop immediately. In those cases that have been allowed to worsen for several years and have become bleeding hemorrhoids or blind piles, improvement will be seen in five days to a week, and a cure probably in two or three weeks.

Menstrual Irregularities and Cramps

When women undergo physical exams, they are generally asked about their periods. This is because menstruation is one gauge of general female health. If the menstrual cycle tends to fluctuate, there is probably an abnormality somewhere in the body. The same is true when a menstrual cycle that is usually regular suddenly starts to become unpredictable.

In order to tell exactly why the irregularity is occurring, you must consult your physician. Here I would like to suggest a method for curing some of the side effects that such irregularities can cause, such as sore shoulders or pain in the lower back. The method is abdominal massage (see p. 94). The two symptoms, menstrual irregularity and constipation, often occur together, and with massage, the flow of blood to the uterus and ovaries increases, solving most problems.

But stubborn irregularities may require more than abdominal massage. In those cases, one can also apply the technique for curing circulatory arrhythmia. This should be done in the morning on days with pleasant weather, in an area with as clean air as possible. Perform the exercise as follows:

1. Sit with your legs stretched out in front of you, and while slowly exhaling the unclean air through your mouth, extend both hands in front of you.

2. After exhaling completely, slowly inhale through your nose and at the same time pull your arms to your sides, bending the elbows. Just before you begin to grow uncomfortable, exhale and spread your arms in front again.

Repeat this process three times, as slowly as you can. Use the ab-

Sit with your legs stretched in front, and while slowly exhaling through the mouth extend both arms.

While inhaling through the nose, bring both arms back to your sides.

dominal massage technique concurrently once a day for a week. Your menstrual cycle should return to normal and the pain will vanish. But do not try the exercise during your period.

Menopause

Though the exact time varies with the individual, menopause or "change of life" occurs in most women between forty and fifty years of age. When that happens, the balance of male and female hormones in the body changes, giving rise to various side effects. These can be unpleasant, involving sore shoulders, pain in the lower back, irritability, labile emotions, and insomnia. These symptoms in turn can have psychological ramifications.

The side effects of menopause are actually caused by aging, and they can be turned around by dōin. Youthful vitality can be restored. Here is how:

1. Sit in the tanbanza position and take one breath.

2. While exhaling through the nose, cross your arms and strongly grip the opposite kneecaps.

3. While holding your breath, release your kneecaps and put one hand over the other. With the palm of the hand that is underneath, give two light taps to each side of your abdomen, then exhale through your mouth.

Repeat this cycle from three to seven times. Hold your breath until just before it becomes uncomfortable, then let it out through the mouth. The precise length of time each person can hold her breath varies; for some, therefore, three cycles will be enough, and for others, five. Do not go overboard. But when you tap your abdomen, never fail to do so twice on both sides.

If you begin this practice in your late thirties, your complexion will stay fresh even in your sixties, and it will keep that youthful luster.

Sit in the tanbanza position and take a breath.

While inhaling through the nose, cross your arms and strongly grip the opposite kneecaps.

With the palm of the hand underneath, lightly tap twice on both sides of the abdomen.

Even if menopause has already started, try the exercise morning and evening for a month. Your family and friends will be amazed by the beneficial effects.

Teeth Grinding, Snoring, Talking in Your Sleep

Many complaints that are not considered diseases by the conventional medical community are treated as such in dōin. Snoring is one such complaint. This includes those who snore habitually as well as those who only do so when they are overtired. I find that of ten people, all ten snore at some time or other, to some degree, and two or three exhibit severe symptoms. The cause of snoring is empyema, the accumulation of purulent matter. The cure, therefore, is to remove that matter through the use of the dōin technique for pollen allergies and rhinitis introduced on page 102.

Teeth grinding (bruxism) is often found among those who are high strung. This too is actually a disease the origins of which are found in irregularities of the cervical vertebrae. It can damage the teeth themselves as well as their alignment. The technique for treating it is the same as that for "middle-aged shoulders" (see p. 91). Try it for ten days and your teeth-grinding will stop.

Talking in your sleep is also considered an abnormality in dōin thought. It occurs when one is not sleeping soundly, when your body wants to sleep but your mind doesn't—when it won't let go of the unpleasant events of the day. It is, in a word, an altered form of insomnia. Treat it using the technique called "The Dragon's Sleep" introduced on page 106.

Since all three complaints are also annoying to others, try the following exercise when you start to feel tired:

1. Sitting either in banza (or tanbanza) style or in a chair, place both hands on the back of your head.

2. Slowly but firmly move your head upward and downward. When you look up, slowly exhale harmful ki through the mouth.

While sitting, place both hands on the back of the head.

While exhaling through the mouth, slowly bend the head upward.

While inhaling through the nose, slowly bend the head forward.

3. When you bend your head down, breathe in slowly through your nose. Perform the entire cycle three to five times to prevent the above symptoms before they start.

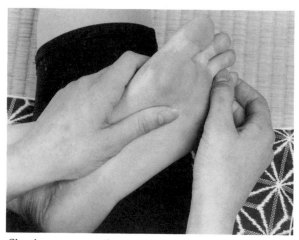
Slowly massage each toe.

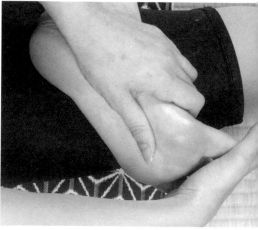
Move all five toes forward and backward.

Athlete's Foot and Corns

People who spend their days in offices obviously have little time in their schedules when they can expose their bare feet to fresh air. After dressing in the morning, ten or even fifteen hours may pass before they can remove their shoes and socks and let their feet breathe. Even those who can change their footwear at the office usually continue to wear their socks. Nor do they exercise their feet much. No matter how much you walk, for example, your toes move relatively little. For this reason, the circulation of ki-rich blood is impaired, even leading in some cases to dying skin. The result is athlete's foot and corns.

According to dōin medical thinking, athlete's foot and corns are both caused when cells die due to the deleterious effects of internally generated harmful ki that can accumulate due to poor circulation of ki-rich blood. In the case of athlete's foot too, the suppurating flesh may spread to the point where the entire toe seems ready to fall off the foot. But there is no need for worry, because no matter how severe the corns or athlete's foot, the condition can be completely cured by improving the circulation of ki-rich blood through exercising the feet and toes.

When you exercise the extremities to stimulate blood circulation, you will find that not only are athlete's foot and corns cured but that your general health improves. This is because stimulation of the feet and toes has the effect of revivifying the circulation of ki-rich blood throughout the system. The technique to use is the same one explained earlier for high and low blood pressure (see p. 108).

This is another exercise you can try that is particularly good for

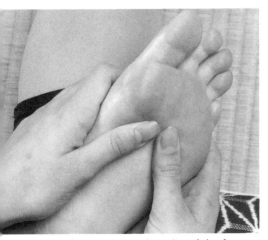

Apply pressure to the soles of the feet.

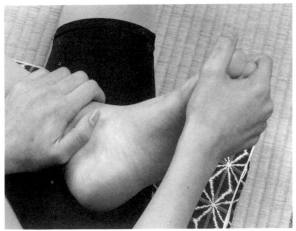

Turn your ankles to the left and right.

Sit with one leg stretched out and the other crossed over it.

corns. It is most effective when used in the bath. Try to do it whenever you can find the time. If you can practice it for a total of two or three hours a day, in a week your athlete's foot or corns will be gone. Try it in any comfortable position, while watching television, for example. Athlete's foot also responds well if you immerse the affected area in lukewarm vinegar for a moment or two before massage.

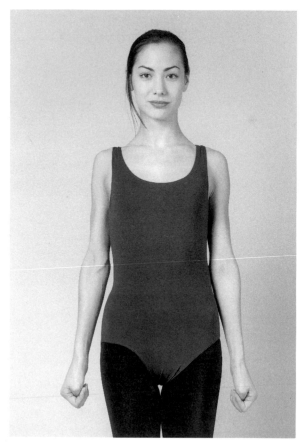

Stand straight with hands at side.

Lace fingers with palms up.

Underarm Odor

Summer is the season when we all begin to worry about body odor. And the more we worry, the worse it gets. Those in high-pressure industries like the media or computers are particularly prone. When you get keyed up, your circulation worsens, the stomach feels heavy, and your internal organs become debilitated.

Particularly offensive is underarm odor. Few modern jobs require us to raise our arms much, and this can result in the ki under the arms stagnating. It is therefore helpful to try this method of "underarm breathing" whenever possible.

1. While standing up straight, lace the fingers of both hands together in front of you, palms up.

2. While exhaling through the mouth, raise your arms above your head, turning your hands over as you do.

Exhale while raising the arms.

3. Raise your arms as high as possible and look up at the backs of your hands.

4. When you have exhaled completely, close your mouth and return the arms to their original position.

This technique will return your sagging, debilitated internal organs to their proper position. Those with stomach or abdominal problems will also benefit, as will women's complexions.

For the interested reader, the Nihon Dokan Web site can be found at http://www.bekkoame.or.jp/i/nihondokan/english/.

APPENDIX

THE SAKE BATH

The Wonderful Effects of Sake

The main reason we become overweight is the accumulation of harmful ki and toxins. When we say that we are having trouble losing weight, what we really mean is that we are not able to return to our original body type. The sake bath is a very effective antidote.

When you take a sake bath, your pores open and expel harmful ki. The blood is then freed of impurities and, together with ki, flows clean and pure throughout the body. The internal organs are stimulated and toxins are expelled. Even if you happen to overeat, the excess calories are eliminated and you do not put on weight.

Sake absolutely works wonders. Most people grow a bit flushed when they drink, which indicates that the flow of ki-rich blood has been improved. As suggested by the old saying that "sake is the best of a hundred medicines," drinking in moderation warms the body, relaxes the spirit, and brings about numerous healthful effects.

But sake is also a strong stimulant. Someone who has never drunk any before may overdo it and vomit or even pass out. But once one learns one's limit, one can enjoy sake's pleasantly heady effects.

Drinking sake in moderation stimulates the circulation of ki-rich blood. But drinking to excess harms the liver and gastrointestinal tract. The sake bath is an ideal way to avoid these harmful side effects while still profiting from sake's benefits.

Sake can also be used effectively in massage treatments. This too is a secret teaching of dōin that has been handed down over five thousand years in China. It can have amazing effects for women in particular, improving the complexion and purifying the internal organs.

Sake appears from time to time in the Chinese medical classic *The Essence of Medical Prescriptions* (*I Hsin Fang*) in the context of sexual techniques. The courtesans in the ancient Chinese palace considered sake baths one of their beauty secrets.

In Japan, sake was widely used by warriors as a disinfectant for wounds. This common use was adopted in modern times by Yazawa Ken'ichi, who used to play for the Chūnichi Dragons baseball team. He successfully treated career-threatening inflammation of the Achilles tendon with sake massage.

How to Make a Sake Bath

Here is the way to prepare a sake bath in your regular bathtub at home. Fill the tub in the normal way with water of the usual temperature. Just before getting into the bath, pour in 0.9 liters (0.95 quarts) of sake and stir it thoroughly. Cheaper low-grade sake is perfectly all right, and sake especially meant for use in the bath is also on the market.

When your body is nice and warm, get out of the tub and wash yourself. When you are nice and clean, then get back in and enjoy a long, warming soak.

When you finish bathing, it is important to wipe yourself off completely with a dry towel, especially your head, armpits, and genitals, since wet hair invites colds. Also be careful about the water temperature. Run the water at a comfortable temperature, and avoid making it too hot—certainly no higher than 42 degrees centigrade (about 108 degrees Fahrenheit). This holds true for baths with or without sake. Higher temperatures invite diseases of the circulatory organs and are not conducive to longevity. Sake baths are very effective in warming the body, and normal bath temperatures work fine even for those who normally like their baths very hot.

Note too that sake baths are extremely powerful cleansers and can leave the bath water very dirty. If you leave the water in the tub for several hours after getting out, you may find that the water is milky with grime, so don't save the water for a second bath even though it may seem a waste. As you repeat the process, you will find the dirt in the tub decreases, and at that point you can reheat the water (if you have a Japanese-style bath that allows you to do so), add another half-liter of sake, and use the water for a second day, but no more.

Activating the Bath with Sake

Bathing is wonderful for your health. Here is why:

1. The heat of the water warms the body.

2. Water pressure pressurizes the body, according to water depth. We are not usually conscious of this effect, but it stimulates the tsubo all over the body, much as does shiatsu massage.

3. Water buoyancy lightens the body, making it easier to move. This is particularly useful for rehabilitation.

In dōin terms, points one and two above improve the circulation of ki-rich blood. But normal baths have only a mild stimulating effect, and it is therefore necessary to raise the temperature of the water or lengthen immersion time to heat the body to its core. But long immersion burdens the heart and circulatory organs, as does very hot water. The sake bath, by contrast, heats the body through and through and improves the circulation of ki-rich blood without requiring over-heated water or long immersion time.

Water itself contains ki. The term "living water" refers to this aspect of its nature. But when you heat water, it loses its ki—you might say it becomes "dead water" through the heating process. By adding sake, you supplement the ki lost in the heating process.

Through the actions of temperature, pressure, and buoyancy, the ki of the sake is transmitted to the body's core. Immersed in a sake bath, one absorbs sake ki through the pores, without becoming intoxicated.

The sake bath also relieves fatigue. We become tired because muscle activity releases fatigue-causing chemicals into the body. It is only very recently that the action of these chemicals has been understood by modern science. But it has been known for centuries in dōin medicine, which refers to it as harmful ki. Dōin practitioners did not analyze the composition of this harmful ki, but over the years they carefully researched ways to stimulate the body and remove it from the system. One such technique is the sake bath, which cures fatigue by improving the circulation of ki-rich blood and eliminating harmful ki through the action of the ki contained in the sake itself.

There is another reason why sake baths are effective in countering fatigue, and that is because of their gentle effect on the skin. When the skin is stimulated too strongly in a normal bath, you may get out of the tub feeling more tired than when you got in. But a sake bath stimulates the skin very gently and so cures fatigue and at the same time soothes away muscle tension. Take one before bed to enjoy a night of deep, restful sleep.

Note: Despite the normally beneficial effects of sake baths, they should be avoided by those with skin diseases, childhood asthma, rheumatism, paralysis, diabetes, or high blood pressure. While the stimulating effects of sake baths are quite mild for healthy people, they can be too strong for people with weakened constitutions and may therefore be counterproductive.